The Great English Earthquake

Peter Haining is a full-time writer whose books have been published in England, America and throughout much of the rest of the world. Previously a journalist and publisher, he brings to his work the resources of an extensive personal library of books and periodicals.

Peter Haining is married with three children and lives in rural Suffolk.

for Margaret —
A 'local' story you
might enjoy!

With Love,

The Great English Earthquake

PETER HAINING

ROBERT HALE · LONDON

Copyright © Peter Haining 1976
First published in Great Britain 1976
First paperback edition 1991
Reprinted 2002
ISBN 0-7090-4391-0

Robert Hale Limited
Clerkenwell House
Clerkenwell Green
London EC1R OHT

Printed by Gutenberg Press Limited, Malta

Contents

For Pop Wenlock
who first told me the story

Illustrations

IN TEXT

Preface to the First Edition

This is a remarkable, but true story. All the events, people and places are real, and the words and statements attributed to those who appear in these pages are the ones which they actually spoke or wrote. No part of the book has been invented and only the slightest dramatic licence has been employed in a few important situations for the sake of clarification. A few opinions and theories have been introduced, however, and except where otherwise stated these are my own and stand or fall by the reader's judgement.

The photographs and illustrations which I have collected will, I am sure, serve to underline the amazing nature of the story and surely put to shame all those who have claimed that 'such things can't happen'? I have also taken particular pains in establishing the facts about the number of deaths attributed to the earthquake, and am convinced that my findings will once and for all set the record right about this extraordinary and unexpected event.

PETER HAINING
Birch Green, Essex

"The Essex Earthquake of 1884 was the most destructive ever known in Britain and was felt as far away as Exeter in the west and beyond York in the north, not to mention in Europe. But it was not the first British earthquake; nor, contrary to popular belief, are such events uncommon ... The history of the event is sufficient to prove, however, that British earthquakes can be more than mere harmless curiosities."

THE TIMES
January, 1975

Preface to the Paperback Edition

History has a habit of playing curious tricks of coincidence. On the day I originally finished writing this book, January 17th 1975, the south coast of England suffered a mild earthquake; and in the week I was informed there was to be a new edition, Britain suffered the biggest earthquake of this century, secondly only to the event which is the subject of this work. The 20 second quake, at 2.46 p.m. on April 2, 1990, was measured at 5.2 on the Richter scale and from its epicentre in North Wales was felt as far away as London, Liverpool, Edinburgh, Bristol and Exeter, and caused the evacuation of people from buildings in the West Midlands and the Black Country, damage to property in Shropshire, Clwyd, the Wirral and Manchester, and the hasty calling-out of staff from the Lucas Aerospace building near Birmingham when it began to shake. I felt the tremor, too, in my home not far from Colchester, Essex – where I just happened to be celebrating my fiftieth birthday!

At the time I was researching and writing this book in the early seventies, I was surprised to discover just how many people believed that earthquakes *never* occurred in Britain. I was also amazed to discover just how much the impact of the 1884 Earthquake had been played down in the newspapers of the time. It was quite clear the authorities in Victorian Britain wanted nothing to suggest that the heart of the great British Empire was subject to such 'foreign' disasters as major earth tremors. Yet the evidence of the reports which were published in the county and local press of the time – plus the remarkable pictures which were taken by a number of alert photographers – reveal that not only was this an earthquake of substantial proportions but just one of numerous such tremors that had occurred throughout the history of our island race. This attitude was in stark contrast to that of the modern press, which made the 1990 tremor front-page news: *The Times* headlined its report on April 3rd, 'QUAKE SECOND BIGGEST FOR OVER 100 YEARS' and the tabloid *Today* declared under a banner headline:'QUAKE BRITAIN – ALL WE NEED NOW IS A PLAGUE OF LOCUSTS'! (*The Times* cartoonist, Mel Calman, incidentally, continued to perpetrate the idea that earthquakes never happened in Britain with his amusing little comment on the news, reprinted here.)

When *The Great English Earthquake* was first published I was delighted with the response it received. The many little titbits of information I had been sent by people all over East Anglia in response to my appeals for stories about the quake were supplemented by further tales which served to underline that the story was no exaggeration, that the people living in the east Essex area, which was the epicentre, had really believed for a few terrible minutes that their world was tumbling all around them. I had the satisfaction, too, of seeing my research into the number of deaths caused by the disaster incorporated into a new entry in the *Guinness Book of Records*; and other facts taken up for more detailed research by organizations as far flung as the Imperial College of Science and Technology in London and the Department of Scientific and Industrial Research in Wellington, New Zealand. A musical stage production, *The Great Colchester Earthquake*, retelling the story in song, verse and dance was also produced by Jonathan Seath and successfully toured in eastern England.

All the evidence suggests that earthquakes will continue to be experienced in the British Isles with varying degrees of intensity. Indeed, a recent report from the British Geological Survey says that in the last ten years England and Wales have been hit by more than sixty earth tremors that have registered more than 2.5 on the Richter scale. However, quite whether we shall ever again experience anything so dramatic and far-reaching as the events on April 22nd 1884, is a matter that only time can answer.

Peter Haining
Boxford, April 1990

1 Earthquake in England!

It sounded like the crack of doom.

A low, rumbling noise that built to a terrifying intensity and then caused the ground to oscillate, turning towns, villages and the whole countryside into great waves of movement like a storm-tossed sea. Buildings and churches swayed and crumbled, houses and cottages shook open in explosions of smoke and debris, and, in a moment more, a terrified and panic-stricken population took screaming to the streets.

Such is the traditional and horrifying pattern of an earthquake. To the people of the British Isles it is a word that conjures up thoughts of the Pacific Islands and far corners of the earth: yet the nation has had a number of seismic disturbances and small quakes during its long history, culminating in the awful and devastating Great English Earthquake of April 22nd 1884.

"The Earthquake of 1884", the renowned scientist and geographer, Professor Charles Davison, has written, "is remarkable as the most destructive known in this country and as visiting a district hitherto free from disturbances."

In less time that it takes to read the above words, the quake had shaken half of England, created widespread destruction, and, although it was stated to the contrary at the time, several deaths. An anonymous and quite impartial eyewitness writing a week later in the parish magazine of Brightlingsea Church, not many miles from the centre of the quake, described it thus:

It was about 9.20 a.m. that a peculiar and alarming noise was suddenly heard, which to some, seemed to be overhead, to others, underground, and which has been variously compared to distant thunder, to the rumbling of a heavy wagon, to the discharge of a volley of Infantry, or to the whirring of a huge flock of birds as they rise from the ground. Immediately afterwards one was conscious of the heaving of the ground or floor beneath one's feet, and of the swaying to and fro of walls, houses, and all kinds of fixed objects. Doors opened and shut, bells rang, articles tumbled

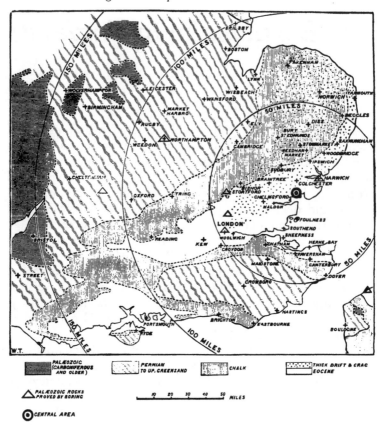

The extent of the earthquake showing main towns affected. An
illustration from *Nature* magazine

from their shelves, and outdoors, bricks, tiles, chimneys, etc.
began to clatter down.

The noise seemed loudest indoors, but perhaps the experience
of those who were standing still in the open air was yet more
alarming, for they could see the solid earth, as well as whatever
was upon it, tremble and heave up and down. In some places, the
earth even in the Scripture phrase, 'Opened her mouth'.

The earthquake on that spring morning was centred on the
rural farming district just to the south-east of Colchester –
Britain's oldest recorded town, the ancient fortification of
Camulodunum. From here it spread with enormous speed and

disturbance over an area of 53,000 square miles. To the north it reached as far as Altrincham in Cheshire, 180 miles away; to the south as far as picturesque Freshwater on the Isle of Wight more than 135 miles away. To the east it was registered in Europe at Ostend in Belgium (100 miles) and Boulogne, France (90 miles), while to the west the shock travelled all of 170 miles to Street in Somerset.

Its impact was experienced within a radius of 150 miles overall, shattering more than 1,200 buildings, including business premises, churches, mansions and hundreds of small houses and cottages, not to mention damaging thousands more and making hundreds of people – including virtually the entire population of one village – homeless. Huge fissures opened in the ground, enormous waves swept along rivers, swamping small boats and spilling over the banks. In the towns people were thrown to the ground, rained with falling debris and overtaken by giddiness, nausea and vomiting. Workmen fled from factories as roofs caved in, children fell panic-stricken from their classrooms, and housewives clutching infants and babies stumbled in terror from their homes. Panic was widespread, confusion was everywhere and, soon, rumours of the cause were as rife as they were improbable.

In less than a minute Britain had experienced one of the most remarkable events in her history; and Essex was left with scars which she bears to this day.

Although there were no instrumental records of the shock taken at the time, scientists and geographers later making deductions based on the great Lisbon Earthquake of 1755, calculated it to have been about one twentieth of the strength of that monstrous European upheaval, and that in the international designation of 1st, 2nd and 3rd class earthquakes this fell "intermediate between 2nd and 3rd class".

Yet for all its magnitude, the Great English Earthquake is to this day one of the forgotten chapters of British history, scarcely known outside the environs of Colchester, documented in only a few days of contemporary newspaper accounts and one official report. It requires and deserves a history of its own and for such reasons was this study written.

My book has its beginnings in the simplest possible way: a chance remark about it in the small Essex village of Birch where I live – which stands not far from the centre of the earthquake – set me off on the quest for the facts and stories which now fill its pages. It has been a fascinating enquiry, built on the dust-laden files of old newspapers, the formal report of a society of amateur archaeologists, and the memories of a handful of surviving old people who, as small children, were actual eyewitnesses to the devastation. To this has been augmented by the recollections of Essex people who heard mention of the topic from their parents and grandparents, painstaking burrowing through parish records and church registers, and detection work among family scrapbooks, official documents, and the minutes of council meetings.

It has been a satisfying as well as a fascinating search, for the passage of time has left only the tiniest number of living witnesses, and the years, too, have made sceptics of succeeding generations of Essex people. The newspaper files, also, are now of the utmost rarity, and the natural processes of decay are busy confining much other documentary material to final oblivion. I suspect, therefore, that if this history, even with its faults, had not been written now, another few years – the centenary, perhaps, in the strangely foreboding year of 1984? – might have been too late. Certainly my intervention has resulted in the re-discovery of a number of extremely frail but absolutely remarkable photographs and drawings made at the time, which I hope will finally serve to brush away from the minds of a modern audience any doubts they may have about the veracity of the story.

My researches, as you will read, have not only enabled me to reconstruct, through eyewitness accounts, what it was actually like during the earthquake, but pose a number of pertinent questions which, in the cause of historical accuracy, need to be asked. For instance, why did so many of the national newspaper statements and official comments at the time play down the amount of damage? – the photographs alone instantly expose this misrepresentation. And why do they insist there was no loss of life as a result of the shock when there quite evidently was?

Why, too, did no one heed the several warnings predicting disaster which were based both on local presentiments and some preliminary seismic activity in the preceding weeks? And what truth, if any, was there in the stories of strange 'red lights' being seen in the sky just before the devastation, and which so fascinated Charles Fort, the American investigator of bizarre phenomena?

Also, how many actual shocks were there – just one or several? And did the earthquake last for "less than three seconds", to quote one witness, or "not less than half a minute", according to another?

And why, when afterwards the appeal fund was launched to raise money for the victims, were donations so slow in coming in? Did the majority of the population, normally so generous in giving to foreign earthquake tragedies, simply not believe, as has been suggested, that such a thing could happen in Queen Victoria's Great Britain?

These, and other questions, will be examined in the light of modern research and analysis in the following pages, after we have first looked briefly at the social and historical background to our story.

England, and indeed the whole of the United Kingdom, was enjoying a period of great prosperity and international influence in the 1880s. The famed British Empire 'on which the sun never set' was at its most powerful and far-reaching, and the strength of the British character was a by-word throughout the civilized world.

The nation, and indeed the whole empire, was now much relieved that the queen had at last returned to public life after her long 'retirement' following the death of her much loved Prince Consort, Albert, in 1861. Victoria's skilful and perceptive Prime Minister, Disraeli, had played a significant part in underlining once again the country's wide-ranging importance and the queen's own position therein by proclaiming her Empress of India in 1876.

While abroad there were the constant stirrings of rebellions and unease – the massacres in Armenia, the revolution in Mexico and the terrible famine in China – in England men and women in most classes enjoyed affluence and prosperity.

Business flourished, British trading was welcomed throughout the world, and the harsh, though benevolent, paternalism of employers at least ensured jobs for all those not afraid of hard work.

It was a time of tranquility, when Englishmen and women could look with pride at any map and, though they would probably never see any of its far-flung outposts, bask in the reflected glory of their nation's power. Day followed day in unruffled calm, and if there was fault to be found in the country's attitude it was in the almost unshakable complacency. There were, of course, the occasional agitators and campaigners who attempted to raise up a desire for change, but the whole climate of serene prosperity frustrated most of their efforts.

This is not to suggest there was no progress: invention, exploration, research and discovery went on at a cracking pace. There were great developments in the area of social welfare, new means of transport brought people within days of each other instead of weeks, and the highly mechanised press, aided by the telegraph and telegram, brought news from every quarter within hours of its happening.

It was against this background that the Great English Earthquake fell like the crack of doom on that April day in 1884.

As the historian Ronald Blythe has written, "We who are conditioned to calamity – wedded to it, one might almost say – have little idea of what a great storm, a shipwreck or the Tay Bridge disaster, for example, meant to our grandparents, the Victorians. Theirs was an age in which, although so much occurred in the broad, progressive sense, the months and days maintained a gentle tenor of existence as far removed from our own complicated times as the dreams of Atlantis." To these people, says Mr Blythe in example, the stories of disaster and trouble from abroad "were the inevitable consequences of not being British. To the country at large, their description in the newspapers remained as unimpressive as a definition of toothache to one who has not suffered."

So, when the earthquake fell, not on some Far Eastern island or even the American continent, but right beneath their very feet, the effect was shattering. Firstly, on the country as a whole, and secondly, and more particularly still, on the county of Essex. Ronald Blythe describes the first effect thus, "The great Essex earthquake had a remarkable effect upon the materialistic complacency of the age, receiving an astonished press and filling the churches with anxious worshippers who feared that such disturbances followed a serial pattern."

It also devastated that particular Victorian idyll that anything made of bricks and mortar was somehow sacred. Looking at the acres of ruined mansions, the broken towns and villages, the Victorian of 1884 saw a blow to the very foundation of his beliefs. Till then he had known only the ruin brought about by time and decay – 'safe as houses' had a very real and potent meaning in his vocabulary.

That the devastation should have fallen on Essex was also another cruel blow: at that time the district was "suffering from an agricultural depression probably more severely than any other part of the Kingdom", to quote one of the inspectors from the Relief Fund Committee who toured the area immediately after the disaster.

But, above all else, this was a tragedy to be measured not just in terms of cause and effect, but in human lives and suffering. On a bright spring morning, England went into the record books with the Shensi Province of China, Lisbon and Alaska as the sufferer of the terrifying phenomenon of a major earthquake.

2 The Destruction of Wivenhoe

The morning of Tuesday, April 22nd 1884 dawned fine and clear. Although the weather had been generally unsettled and there had been some rain on the previous days, the barometer and the thermometer had both risen during the night, and the morning sky was bright with sunshine and there was only the occasional cloud. There was scarcely a breath of wind and the early morning smoke from the chimneys of the little cottages and houses hung in long, white twists against the blue backdrop of the sky.

The little village of Wivenhoe was stirring quietly in the growing warmth of the spring morning, the sailors and fishermen long since at work on their boats along the quay. The dwellings behind them appeared to huddle together on the slope of the Essex landscape as it dipped to the edges of the meandering river Colne. This gently-moving river was nearing the end of its journey from the Essex hinterland as it passed the village on its way to the North Sea, a mere three miles further on.

Along the quayside were moored a variety of small craft: fishing smacks which plied the North Sea for herring and sole or dredged for succulent Essex oysters; small barges laden with timber, rope and general goods for ports along the east coast of England, and various pleasure boats ranging from tiny rowing dinghies to sailing yachts and, moored in the river, one or two larger steam yachts.

Apart from its centuries-old function as a fishing port, Wivenhoe had now become a fashionable yachting centre, drawing amateur and weekend sailors from all over the county and even as far as London. This, naturally, had brought a little prosperity to the community of 3,000 people, for the local fisherfolk could add to their meagre earnings from the sea by crewing for the visiting yachtsmen as well as servicing and

looking after their craft. Money was also to be made by hiring
out mooring berths along the quay and anchorage points in
the river itself: not to mention ferrying the sailors to and from
the larger craft.

On this particular morning the river was high, full tide had
just passed at nine o'clock, and those fishermen who had not
taken to the sea, were idling along the quayside, talking in
small groups or working methodically at repairing their nets.
The doors of a number of the pretty little brick and
weatherboard cottages facing the quay were open, and
housewives were busy shaking out mats and calling their
morning greetings to one another. In several of the attractive
bow-fronted windows of the dwellings cats lay dozing in the
sunshine.

At the door of the Anchor Inn, which stood at the corner of
Anchor Hill and the quay, Mrs Dick Ham, a short, jolly
woman, who had been working with her husband since a little
after dawn to ready the public house for the day's trade,
paused to survey the sunlit view. She looked out across the
street to where the road ended in the hard-standing for Mr
Jones' ferry service across the Colne. The boat at this moment
was just taking on two passengers from the far side of the river,
and as her eyes travelled beyond it to the right she could see
that the little village of Rowhedge on the other side was also a
hive of industry. The ferryman threw off his lines and began
the return trip. Then the sound of glasses being moved behind
her stirred Mrs Ham from her reverie and she went back into
the small bar. It looked set fair for a good day, she thought.

Another small boat, carrying three men, was being rowed
across the Colne, but in the opposite direction to the ferry,
heading for a large, impressive steam yacht moored against
the Rowhedge bank. This vessel, a sleek two-master, bright in
a new coat of dark blue paint, lay motionless at anchor, its
sails and rigging neatly furled and only the merest haze of
smoke rising from its single white funnel. Beneath the
figurehead of a hand-carved flying maiden was the legend,
Santa Cecilia.

Sitting in the stern of the small boat as it progressed steadily
towards the yacht was its owner, a tall, dignified man
immaculately dressed in a navy-blue, double-breasted jacket,

white ducks and a peaked cap. He was Lord Alfred Henry
Paget, a renowned figure in British social and political life. As
the smartly turned-out member of the *Santa Cecilia*'s crew
rowed on in silence, Lord Alfred cast critical eyes over his 300-
ton vessel to see how it had weathered the Atlantic crossing. It
had anchored only half an hour before at Wivenhoe after
journeying from America where he had been using it to cruise
during a well-earned holiday and entertain a number of
friends who lived along the eastern seaboard. Although now
retired, Lord Alfred had had to return earlier than expected to
deal with some business matters and was anxious to see that
the crossing had gone smoothly in his absence. Although not
able to sail as often as he would have liked, he was an
accomplished and skilled sailor able to cope with even the
fiercest Atlantic storm as he had proved on more than one
occasion. Even at sixty-eight years of age, and after a lifetime
moving in the highest and most fashionable circles, he carried
himself firmly and erect and was renowned amongst his crew
members for the strength of his arm.

Lord Henry was the second son of the far-famed Marquis of
Anglesey (1768-1854), a distinguished soldier and military
commander who became Lord Lieutenant of Ireland. The
marquis had earned a place in history for his service with
Wellington at the Battle of Waterloo, and considerable
affection from the public because of great courage shown
when he led a charge against the French, and was wounded in
the leg by one of the last bullets fired in the battle. This
necessitated an almost immediate amputation of the leg, and,
as the *Dictionary of National Biography* remarked in 1895, "the
limb was buried in a garden in the village of Waterloo, a
monument was placed over it, and it is still a source of income
to the proprietor."

The marquis' son, Alfred, had served with similar
distinction in his father's regiment, the 7th Hussars, and was
its general for some years before his retirement in 1881. He
was also for many years chief equerry and clerk-marshall to
Queen Victoria, and a Whig Member of Parliament for the
Lichfield constituency from 1837 to 1865. Throughout his life
he loved sailing, and spent many weekends and holidays on
his various yachts, using Wivenhoe for some years as one of his

favourite berthing points.* It was also a particularly handy place to reach by road or rail from his home in Cavendish Square, London.

On this morning, Lord Alfred had risen before dawn to be driven down to the *Santa Cecilia* so that he could meet the vessel on arrival and make a full inspection. He already had it in his mind to take her out again before the weekend. As the dinghy neared the yacht his keen grey eyes saw that she had made the crossing without any apparent problems and looked to be immediately seaworthy. He smiled with approval at the third man in the boat, Tom Potter, his captain, who sat in the bow.

A few moments more and the dinghy bumped gently against the *Santa Cecilia* and Lord Alfred stepped nimbly up the gangway. The other two men followed him smartly up to the deck where the remaining members of the twenty-strong crew were lined up to greet their employer. He inclined his head slightly, his eyes sweeping the ship to see that all was in place. On an impulse, which he was never quite able to explain afterwards, he turned around to look back at the quay he had just left.

It was at that moment – precisely 9.18 GMT – that it happened.

"As I looked towards the village there was this terrible loud rumbling noise," Lord Alfred said. "Immediately the vessel began to shake and the people around me fell like ninepins. I was flung against the rigging and, clutching on for dear life, wondered if the boiler of the yacht had burst."

As the nobleman was rocked back and forth he was eyewitness to the destruction of Wivenhoe.

First, the whole village seemed to rise up, the red slate roofs moving up and down as if they were the waves of the sea. Then, weaving crazily, chimney stacks began to tumble over, crashing onto the roofs, showers of slates cascading down the sloping inclines of the houses either into the streets or through the huge gaps which appeared in the roofs themselves. "The village was apparently lifted bodily up," said Lord Alfred, at that moment himself being thrown to the deck by a huge wave

---

*Lord Alfred in fact died on one of his yachts, the *Violet*, on August 24th 1888, while he was moored at Inverness.

which swept across the Colne, see-sawing boats, tearing hands from rudders and swamping vessels of all sizes. "And as I fell I saw part of the church steeple, which towers over the village, sway and then topple into the mass of the devastation."

Along the quayside, windows, which had only minutes earlier been cleaned, shattered and showered glass across the street. Cracks ran like angry veins across the white-washed facias, and the dust of thousands of tumbling slates blossomed up into the sky like the smoke of so many small explosions.

"The rumbling noise was almost immediately superceded by the dreadful sound of crashing masonry and the terrible cries of the people. Their shrieks rang out across the water even through all the din," continued Lord Alfred.

All was confusion on the *Santa Cecilia* too; some of the men were trying to get to their feet, hauling themselves up on the bulwarks or clutching on to the wheelhouse, as the huge boat continued to sway from side to side. Several men who had fallen against deck machinery were moaning and clutching hands to their bloodied faces.

The grey, cloying smoke of the falling buildings thickened and swelled around the village, spreading like a fog over the quay where the fishing boats rolled and smashed against each other. Two men up the masts of their small craft were pitched unceremoniously into the water. A sailor on another, who somehow managed to cling on, saw the roof of his own house fall and knew that his wife and young baby were probably inside. Others who had been tending to their nets dropped to the ground as if felled by invisible hands; several toppled screaming from their heaving craft, where they fought desperately against the churning waves.

Walls began to burst outwards, masonry falling in a kind of agonized slow motion on to the quay or into the river itself. Through the smoke the rooms of houses – kitchens, bedrooms, sitting rooms – which moments before had enjoyed the security of four walls were opened up to view as brickwork crumpled and lath and plaster cracked and split open obscenely.

On his feet again, hanging on to the bulwarks, Lord Alfred saw the final agonies of movement as the rumbling decreased. The wave motion had passed – and he realized almost instinctively, what it was that had actually happened. He wanted desperately to disbelieve the evidence of his own eyes. Carnage was everywhere before the astonished sailors. The dust was still rising, masonry fell in occasional bursts, and people were now starting to appear everywhere, some running panic stricken into each other, tumbling over debris, calling agonisedly for some loved one, crying in fear and injury. Even from 100 yards away on the *Santa Cecilia* the horror on every begrimed face could be sensed if not actually seen.

"The cries made us fear for dreadful loss of life," said Sir Alfred, now almost recovered and rapping out orders that all hands were to return to the village to lend what help they could. The vessel was settling again and thoughts could be collected. What had caused this terrible thing? Was it some huge explosion – or an earthquake? To the sailors who had not long returned from America where quakes were a regular occurrence, this seemed the most likely cause.

Their suspicions were soon confirmed by Captain Potter, who had actually witnessed the destruction of Chios in 1881.* Unbelievingly, he said that he had never seen anything to approach that terrible devastation until the sight now before his eyes. Without another word, the crew fell quickly to preparing the boats to cross to Wivenhoe which, by now, was a centre of horror and personal tragedy ...

At *The Anchor*, where Mrs Dick Ham had watched Lord Alfred being rowed to his yacht, she was alone in the bar when the rumbling "like the sound of a traction engine under the floorboards" disturbed the peace of the morning. Immediately thereafter a wave-like motion seemed to lift the sawdust-covered floor of the bar upwards, bulging out the walls as if they were made of elastic and throwing everything that was loose to the ground. "I was flung back against the counter before I could open my mouth," said Mrs Ham. "Glasses began to tumble all around me, the beer casks rolled over with

* The earthquake on the island of Chios happened on April 3rd 1881 when three violent shocks caused the destruction of 45 towns and villages and the loss of over 4,000 lives. Enormous fissures opened in the ground and great landslips occurred on many hills and mountains. There were also further shocks on virtually every succeeding day until April 19th.

a terrible crash, and the doors and windows buckled and broke out. Plaster began to fall from the ceiling all over me, followed by debris and then something struck me from behind which knocked me out."

Beams twisted and split above Mrs Ham as she lay unconscious of the destruction going on all around her. Her last thought before she lapsed into the dark was that one of the steamboats moored near the quay must have exploded. Perhaps Lord Alfred Paget's yacht?

At the rear of *The Anchor*, Mr Dick Ham, a tall, muscular man sporting a huge handle-bar moustache, was tidying up with his young potboy. "It was just like the rush of a train underground. I and my lad stood still, and I said, 'For God's sake, stand,' and the next moment the chimney pots and bricks and tiles came pouring down around us like rain, and how we escaped from being killed outright or seriously injured God alone knows – I don't."

Even a week later Mr Ham was still so dazed by his narrow escape that he could only tell a local newspaper reporter, "My feelings at the time I cannot describe. The crash of the falling buildings simultaneously with the shrieks and cries of those unable to get out of their homes I shall ever remember."

Helped by the youngster, Mr Ham dug frantically through the debris and into his premises to find his wife. She lay where she had fallen unconscious, almost totally covered by plaster and broken wood. Only the feeble movements of her bloodied hands told Mr Ham that she was still alive ...

As Mr Ham reached his wife he couldn't help being conscious of the cries from the other small cottages close by his public house, at what was known as Anchor Corner.

The destruction had been particularly bad in the small grocer's shop belonging to James Moore, a genial and much liked Wivenhoe man whose reputation for generosity was a by-word in the village.

Mr Moore had been checking stock in his cellar when the rumbling seemed to crash against the walls around him, almost deafening him with its intensity. He staggered back against one of the walls covering his ears as the floor and ceiling shook around him. Even as goods tumbled and spilt around him, only the strength of the cellar beams seemed to prevent him from being buried alive.

The same good fortune, however, was not being enjoyed by his two sons who were upstairs working in the small, low-ceilinged shop, packed with its groceries of all descriptions. The younger, Peter, fell under a shower of loose packets, but was shielded from the crashing shelves and heavier tins and jars by the sturdy oak counter.

The older boy, James Moore junior, had just stepped out into the tiny back garden when the trembling started. His bemused eyes looked upwards at the very moment when the three large chimneys on the top of the premises began to lean over and fall. A cry escaped from his lips as he stepped backwards, stumbling over a packing case and sprawling on to a flower bed. He could barely bring his arms up to cover his face before a deluge of tiles, plaster and guttering from the roof submerged him. One of the chimney pots crashed only inches from his head, several of the bricks adding to the rubbish which covered his body and choked his mouth, nose and eyes. Half conscious, he tried feebly to move, and then lay still. It was to be some minutes before the terrified Mr Moore was to find his bleeding and concussed son ...

Next door to the Moore's grocery shop, Mr H.T. Cuthbert, the yacht decorator, who only two months ago had been responsible for the repainting of Lord Alfred's yacht, was collecting his materials together in the hall ready to begin work. Already dressed in his paint-stained overalls, he was just searching for his battered derby hat, which he wore everywhere, when "a sound like a boiler exploding" rocked him off his feet.

As he fell forwards, he saw the walls of his hallway buckle and crack, then the ceiling seemed to open like a gaping mouth and through it crashed part of one of his chimneys. Bricks smashed into the floor and skidded off at all angles, one group still held together by cement cracking into Mr Cuthbert's exposed shins. Waves of pain brought the bile rising from his stomach, and he rolled over clutching shaking fingers at his knees.

In the lounge of his house, the other chimney broke through the ceiling and smashed into the fireplace where Mrs Cuthbert had only half an hour before lit a small fire. She was rooted, horrified, at this moment in her kitchen as the walls cracked, windows splintered, and tiles rattled down like giant hailstones. Miraculously, nothing hit Mrs Cuthbert who, acting by instinct before panic could claim her reason, called out to her husband. Getting no immediate reply she dashed into the hallway and helped up the vomiting man she found on the floor. Together they staggered to the door as the house swayed and buckled around them. Unnoticed, the flaming coals which had been thrown from the fireplace began to set light to the furniture and carpets in the lounge. A few minutes more and the room was a blazing inferno. On the table, forgotten, Mr Cuthbert's favourite brown derby hat was soon little more than a pile of smouldering ashes ...

Around the corner from this group of houses, in West Street, the Independent Chapel shivered as if disturbed by a giant hand. The unpretentious lines of the building reflected in many ways the reserved and devout manners of its small community of worshippers, not a few of whom had helped raise the money for its construction in 1846. Sturdily built on solid foundations, it was, nevertheless, no match for the oscillation of the ground which boomed beneath it.

The vestry was badly shattered by the blow, and the stone copings and ornamental parapet were demolished. Inside, walls cracked and buckled, and the plaster ornamentation in the centre of the ceiling fell. Lath and plaster tumbled on to the pulpit, smashing over chairs and destroying in an instant all the hard work of the previous day when a group of helpers had worked to prepare the chapel for a mid-week service.

In the ceiling the gas point, from which a chandelier had just fallen, began to hiss gently. Soon the atmosphere grew fetid and sickly – it would only take a carelessly struck match by an anxious salvager to cause the most terrible explosion ...

Adjacent to the chapel, Mr George Stebbing, Wivenhoe's other grocer, was busy in his shop erecting a precarious pyramid of tinned lobster in the window. He had a fine view from this window – how often had people commented on it? – down Quay Street to the river Crouch, and as he worked he could see the little boat carrying Lord Alfred Paget out to the *Santa Cecilia* moving steadily through the water. He hummed quietly to himself as he worked, enjoying the sun on his pink, well-scrubbed hands and bald head.

"When the earthquake came I did not know what it was," he said later, "but I heard the house rattling, the tins of lobster and salmon rolled about the shop by scores, and things were tumbling down in all directions. I felt myself reeling and caught hold of one of the iron pillars, thinking I was going to be buried alive where I stood."

Moments later, when a stunned and shaking Mr Stebbing hurried out into the road he saw that there was not a single house or shop in West Street which had not had its windows smashed, its roof untiled or its chimneys broken down. He stood for some time in the debris which covered the road, rubbing his hands down his white apron, unable to comprehend what he saw ...

The quake struck with as terrifying force as anywhere at the red-bricked National School in Wivenhoe High Street. The seventy bright-eyed, red-cheeked children, the girls neat in their smocks and the boys in little grey jackets, had just finished assembly when the noise was heard. The cracking of the walls was followed by the heaving of the floors and startled cries were mingled with the sound of falling bodies and scurrying feet amidst the enveloping dust and debris. Only the presence of mind of the school's quiet and austere headmaster, Mr Collins, prevented a panic-stricken riot of children. He had experienced a "pretty good shock" when in Wales some years before and realized almost immediately what was happening.

"We were just about to begin lessons when the school started rocking," he recalled later, "and the children began to be very much alarmed. I had been in an earthquake before, and knowing at once what it was I checked the children and told them there was nothing to fear. When the shock was passed I got them out of the school as quickly as I could."

Despite the terrible noise and shaking, the structure of the school did not suffer as badly as some other places. The chimney fell, the walls cracked and there was "a terrible mess" everywhere, but the quality of the work of the local craftsmen who had built the school was undoubtedly the saving of their grandchildren. All the children were herded into the playground, quite a number suffering from bruises and small cuts, the first of the anxious parents who had come running from their homes and the shipyards after the shock, swept their sobbing offspring into their arms ...

Not far from the school, standing on a small ridge of high ground and surrounded by delightful park and woodland, stood the imposing Wivenhoe Hall, the home of Mr James Jackson, a well-known Essex figure, city businessman and JP. This mansion, with its fine views over the village and the river towards Rowhedge, provided the setting for another miraculous escape. A young nephew of Mr Jackson had just stepped dripping from his morning bath in one of the upper bedrooms when the shock threw down a chimney weighing nearly two tons, which crashed through the ceiling and fell squarely into the bath, smashing it and flooding water everywhere.

Mr Jackson's statement of the moments of terror for his household read as follows:

> I was in the dining-room this morning, when I felt a shock and heard a rattling as of falling masonry. My first impression was that a chimney had become detached and blown down. The noise, however, continued and I recognised at once that it was an earthquake.
>
> I ran out of the front of the house, and called upon all those within hearing to do the same. As far as I could judge the shock lasted six or seven seconds. As soon as it was over, I returned to the house which I found filled with soot and smoke.
>
> I called one or two others to me and in going over the house I found a great deal of damage. A piece of chimney, some two tons in weight, had fallen through the roof into a bath, which had only just been vacated by the second of a couple of schoolboys home for their holidays.

Inspection showed that the Hall had lost its chimneys, several of which crashed through the roof; the gable at the north end of the building was dismantled; the walls were seriously fissured and cracked; the laundry was badly damaged and also the tower of the stables. The Lodge, where the keeper lived, was also seriously damaged and Mr Jackson had to visit all his servants to quieten them after the shock.

Such was the overall state of the Hall, however, that the master realized it was quite uninhabitable, and he became one

of the first residents of Wivenhoe to decide that he would have
to move his family and household elsewhere – in his case to
London – until extensive repairs could be carried out. For a
time, though, he stood before the mansion, watch in hand,
half expecting there to be another tremor ...

At the top of the High Street, not far from the Hall, a
fifteen-year-old girl, Bessie Mason, observed the upheaval of
her village, almost as an impartial witness.

Young Bessie was out for an early morning walk when she
had paused to look back down over the clustering roofs of
Wivenhoe. It was such a beautiful morning, and she could see
the windows of the shops and houses glinting in the sunshine.
Beyond the tower of the parish church she could see a few of
the buildings of Rowhedge just visible through the trees which
grew along the marshland bordering the river Colne. For a few
moments she watched the local people going about their
business, into the shops or stopping for a chat here and there.
Then she took a deep, appreciative breath of the fresh, still air,
and was about to continue her walk when the ground beneath
her feet shook like waves under a fisherman's boat.

She stood transfixed with fright as the village before her
heaved and trembled. With growing fear she saw chimneys
tumbled from roofs and debris poured on to luckless villagers
who were passing. All around her buildings groaned and
cracked, and her horror was suddenly redoubled when a
chimney pot smashed down beside her.

Bessie let out a cry and began to run down the High Street
towards the home of her father, Captain Robert Mason. She
must get home and make sure that the rest of her family were
alright. Could something have happened at the gas works? she
wondered as she ran – there was always talk in the village
about the possibility of an explosion there. But there was no
time to investigate now ...

The shock had, as was to be expected, greatly damaged the
gas works, but it was not the origin of the disaster as the young
girl thought. The earthquake had torn through the brick
buildings, heaving over the mountains of coal and upending
workers throughout the premises. As men struggled to regain
their feet amidst the enveloping coal dust and falling
materials, the fifty-foot circular brick shaft tottered and two-

thirds of it fell, smashing across the main buildings and hurling masonry into the other storage and engineering buildings around the main yard.

Soon the sound of escaping gas from fractured pipes joined in the cacophany of noise as men fought and struggled to get clear of the buildings and into the open air. One man, overcoming his own fright for a moment, paused just long enough to turn off the main cylinder, thereby sealing off the gas in the damaged, but not fractured, main gasometer. The action of this anonymous hero undoubtedly prevented a major escape of gas and probably a flash explosion.

Emerging into the sunlight from the choking fumes of the gas works, the employees could see that devastation lay all around them. A man and woman who had fallen in the street implored a worker with torn shirt and bloodied head who ran past them whether the gas cylinder had exploded ...

All around the neighbourhood of the gas works there was confusion and fear. Along the High Street, in Brook Street, in New Road, and among the other side-turnings, where houses and cottages stood packed together in tight little rows, roofs had tumbled down, walls cracked open and debris lay ankle-deep everywhere. People were spilling into the streets, some only half-dressed, others caught in the midst of a morning shave or wash with the soap still wet on their faces and already congealing with the blood from cuts and scratches.

Many eyes turned to Wivenhoe Church, towering over the village, and in an instant a shadow of its former self. The Rector, the Reverend John Baillie, a sturdy, white-haired man, was just walking across the graveyard back to his rectory, when the blow struck. Before his horrified gaze he watched the building he so dearly loved, and which had only been restored in 1860 at the enormous cost of £3,000, quiver and crack.

"The Church presented a very woeful and dilapidated aspect," he remembered a week later. "From the summit of the battlements to the coping some eight feet below the tower, all was shattered, and many tons of stone hurled into the graveyard, most of the blocks nearly burying themselves in the ground.

"The battlements on the north and west sides were also

smashed down into the churchyard, and those on the other side were left so perilously balanced they had to be taken down.

"The Tower is rent in many places, and alongside the northern window of the belfry the solid wall is riven asunder to the width of two or three inches. A quantity of masonry fell into the Church itself, but by God's providence not so much as to ruin it beyond repair."

Good churchman that he was, the Reverend Baillie, although desolate by the ravages on the church and still amazed he had escaped injury himself, went quickly to comfort parishioners he noticed staggering from their houses or running frightened along the streets. It was not the first such devastation he had seen, having been an eyewitness to the Seige of Paris by the Prussians in 1870-1. Then, as now, he knew his strength and prayers would be required by those who had suffered ...

In New Road, the shock had fallen heavily on the lines of red-brick houses, particularly on a group of eight at the lower end which belonged to a local property owner, Mr John Green Chamberlain. Chimneys had tumbled down, the gable at the end of the row had been smashed out, and many of the interiors of the houses opened up by cracks and fissures. Several invalids confined to bed had been rudely awakened, rolled from their beds and half buried by falling debris. In lower rooms, housewives clearing up breakfast things or beginning their morning cleaning were bowled over by the force, crockery and brooms torn from their grasp and dashed to the ground. Domestic pets, until that moment dozing quietly, leapt terror-stricken for cover as masonry crashed around them, both indoors and on the steps where several lay in the sunshine. Small children, including several babies in their prams, howled in fright, as bricks and tiles rained down around them.

Another property owner in the area to suffer heavily was Mr Isaac Blyth whose houses in Brook Street took a particularly hard pounding. Mr Blyth also owned one of Wivenhoe's most popular pubs, the 'Black Boy Inn', at the end of East Street, which like most of his houses became completely untenable after the destruction.

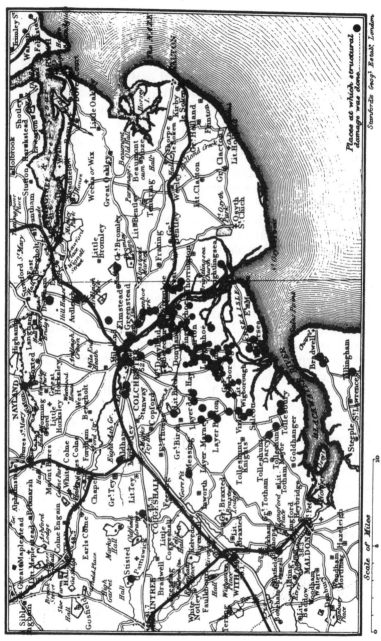

The centre of the earthquake. (The black spots indicate the places which were hardest hit)

All the public houses, in fact, suffered severely, roofs being wrecked, cellars and their contents destroyed, and the bars presenting the appearance of "having been visited by terrible explosions". This being particularly true of *The Ship at Launch* near the quay, *The Anchor, Live and Let Live, Falcon*, the *Sailor's Return* and the *Grosvenor Hotel*. At the hotel, which served meals as well as providing accommodation, the landlord, Mr J. Goodwin, narrowly escaped with his life when its two chimneys crashed into the road just as he was fleeing the premises.

The Post Office, which had just opened for the day's business, had several customers at the moment of shock. The Post Master, Mr J. Pratt, was thrown backwards against his sorting table, going down in a pile of letters, parcels and crashing debris. The customers, rooted in fear, were thrown together in a heap, one old man saving himself from injury by clinging tight to the iron grille on the counter.

At the Almshouses, the aged residents, several of whom were just getting up, were thrown into great alarm. Miraculously, their sturdy dwellings, built over half a century earlier, withstood the quake probably better than most other properties of the same size. Undoubtedly, if it had been more than plaster and some ceiling fittings which fell in these places, there could have been a high death toll ...

It was in the vicinity of the quay, however, that much of the greatest drama of the earthquake had been seen by people who, because they were in the most open part of the town, were free from the danger of falling buildings, and had uninterrupted views.

People like Captain Harry Harlow, a well-known amateur yachtsman, who was sitting on the quay wall looking at his yacht, the *Rosabelle*, at that moment, Captain Harlow, a former career soldier, was a man much sought after by would-be sailors from the gentry of the district, and enjoyed a widespread reputation for his knowledge and the influence he carried in local social and official circles.

The booming sound below ground first caught his attention, then the wave which seemed to lift boats that lay on the mudbank on the Rowhedge side of the river, followed by the craft actually in the water – including Lord Alfred Paget's yacht. Those standing on the stocks in the shipyard "were shifted and rolled about so much that I greatly feared they would be completely destroyed." Almost fortuitously, Captain Harlow was spun round by the 'wave' as it passed under his feet and saw what happened to the entire village.

> I saw the Church and all the houses in the place rocking about, some one way and some another. The only way I can describe it is that the houses looked like a lot of pleasure boats at the seaside, with a ground swell on, with some of the boats rolling in one direction and some another.
>
> The Church appeared to go over several degrees to the South East, and then back again to the North West. When the top of the tower came down with a crash, at the same time the huge chimneys of the Grosvenor Hotel also came down. Looking in all directions I saw chimneys, walls and houses coming down.

Captain Harlow was to play a leading role in the salvage work in Wivenhoe, and it was to him that many of the inhabitants went to ask for outside help in clearing up the devastation. His first thought was of the army and he made contact with Major-General White, the Officer Commanding Eastern District at Colchester, requesting troops to aid in the rescue. The battalion of soldiers who marched in neat formation down Wivenhoe High Street the following morning were accorded the kind of welcome usually reserved for troops relieving a town after years of occupation ...

A second eyewitness from a similar vantage point was another member of the Ham family – who could count themselves among the oldest established in the district – Mr William Ham. A tall, bluff man, who had sailed many of the world's oceans, Mr Ham was no stranger to earthquakes, as his statement made later in the day proved:

> I was on a brig on the river, with my face to the village, and the first indication I had of anything amiss was that the vessel rose into the air. I knew at once that the shock was an earthquake, having experienced similar visitations many times in the Atlantic and in the western isles of the Azores.
>
> Recognising immediately the sensation beneath my feet, I glanced at the shore and saw Dick Ham's chimneys at the eastern extremity come down. As the wave rolled on I saw every chimney

topple, until the work of destruction reached the line of the church tower, and then the crashing masonry raised such clouds of dust that I could see no more, and I thought the whole place had collapsed.

It was quite five minutes before the atmosphere cleared, and then, of course, the extent of the damage stood revealed. To the best of my belief the shock lasted about five seconds, and it seemed to travel from north to south.

Although I was badly shaken I hurried ashore. As I stumbled up the road the devastation that met my eyes was horrifying. It was something I had only ever expected to see far from our shores.

As Mr Ham ran along the quay, he passed the bewildered figure of one of his friends, Mr Edwin Wilkins, a local yacht builder, who had just emerged from his yard. He, too, was to record his experiences graphically in an interview the following day.

At the time of the disturbance, Mr Wilkins had been standing near the stern of the *Medora* a new 175-ton yacht which was shored up on stocks. He heard a rumbling sound and the boat "plunged in a fore and aft direction". Before his horrified eyes, the vessel was lifted bodily off the block and thrust over. Buildings around him began "to crack and snap all the way along", and other yachts in the yard began to fall off their stocks. As he staggered back, the chimney and part of the gable at the end of his joiner's shop were thrown down and broke through the roof of a shed, smashing a three-ton yacht beneath.

"The chimney seemed to fall in slow motion," said Mr Wilkins, "it broke off and described a slight curve in the air, the upper part coming down undermost."

Mr Wilkins, to whom careful observation and exactness of measurement were second nature, was able to record the extraordinary 'wave' motion of the earthquake by what happened to the buildings which formed his workshop and at which he was looking.

"I was standing thirty feet from and looking at, the row of buildings which run in a direction North East to South West. Along the upper part of the buildings, which are thirty feet high, there is a row of windows belonging to the workshops facing North West and a corresponding row runs along the opposite (South East) face of the buildings overlooking Bath Street which bounds the yard on this side.

"Under ordinary circumstances, an observer standing in the yard at the point I was, could not see through the upper windows and across the buildings into Bath Street, as the line of vision falls on to the roof about three feet above the highest part of the window on the Bath Street side of the workshops.

"At the moment of shock, however, I was enabled to see *through both windows*, and observed the fall of the chimney and brickwork from a house in Bath Street opposite the workshops. Taking as data my own height and distance from the buildings, and the height of the opposite windows above the ground, I must have been lifted vertically to the extent of three feet while the building was depressed to the same extent, and tilted over towards me at an angle of five degrees.

"I therefore believe that the surface wave in solid earth of the earthquake had the enormous amplitude of six feet!"

Mr Wilkins' statement is one of the very few accounts to attempt to measure the 'wave' of the disturbance – and because of his profession and integrity it caused much discussion subsequently among scientists and geographers.

One such expert, Professor James Taylor, who actually spoke to Mr Wilkins and had him draw a diagram of what he saw, was inclined to accept his statement as he wrote in *Hardwicke's Science Gossip* in June 1884: "Its accuracy is unquestionable," he said, "and the fact observed can hardly be denied, coming as it does from an observer whose daily professional avocation leads him to deal with exact measurements."

Yet, the weight of scientific discussion found the claim to be "impossible". "The amount of displacement cannot be admitted," wrote J. Edmund Clarke in the *Natural History Journal* of that same month. Only one authority, however, had a solution to offer for the phenomenon. He was Professor J.A. Ewing, a seismologist, who believed that the buildings had a certain 'elasticity' which meant that only part of it – in this case the top half – was twisted, in such a way that Mr Wilkins saw what he did without the surface movement being anything like as much as he calculated.

Said the professor, "A series of small horizontal movements

of the base will often produce a large accumulation vibration on the part of the superstructure, especially if the roof is heavy, and the construction such as to admit of distortion. In a frame house, without cross-bracing, and with a heavy roof, there is nothing to prevent the swing of the roof being a foot or two in amplitude or even more, though the movements of the base may be fractional parts of an inch."

Professor Ewing admitted this theory could not be held as irreversible, and Mr Wilkins refused to be budged from his conclusion about the largeness of the earthquake 'wave'. And to this day it has proved impossible to refute his verdict ...

Only minutes, in fact, passed before the first medical aid reached the village in the form of a local doctor, Dr H.C. Sorby, who had actually been out sailing in his yacht when the blow fell.

Dr Sorby, a skilled and enthusiastic local sailor, was well-known for his early morning trips before surgery. This morning he had set out with his yacht, *Glimpse* for a brisk sail up the tributary of the Colne, the Roman River, which left it at right angles just in front of Wivenhoe. He was on his way back, and had anchored about half a mile from East Donyland for some breakfast, when he heard a large booming sound and the boat was moved violently forwards to the west and then even more violently backwards to the east.

Seated as he was below decks in the cabin, Dr Sorby had no time to react to the blow and was thrown against the bulwark where he cracked his head and was knocked unconscious. Up on deck, the doctor's pilot struggled to regain control of the craft as the water waved alarmingly around him. Like every other sailor at the rudder of his craft – whatever the size – the pilot had the experience of being quite unable to steer the boat, and had the impression of being "on a rock, bumping violently".

When he had the yacht in control, the pilot called to Dr Sorby and, getting no reply, went into the cabin. It took him only a matter of moments to revive the stunned physician, and then both went on deck to try and establish what had been the cause. One glance down the river at Wivenhoe, which was shrouded in dust, was enough to convince them that a serious tragedy had occurred.

While the doctor applied a simple bandage to his bruised

head, the pilot weighed anchor and steered the *Glimpse* towards Wivenhoe. When he had finished, Dr Sorby began to check through the equipment and medicine he had in his bag. It had always been his practice to take it with him wherever he went, and today he felt it was going to be very much needed ...

In the village, the main task of ministering to the injured had been started quickly and efficiently by the local GP, Dr A.C. Squire Ling. His wife, a nurse and two voluntary workers were already lending a hand as the bruised and the bleeding people came into his surgery. There was going to be no chance of making house calls for a while, Dr Ling thought to himself as he worked quickly and efficiently, and the prayed that the rescue work in the fallen debris would not reveal too many tragedies among these people he had grown so fond of. Here, he bandaged the bleeding head of a man he remembered delivering as a baby – there, was the shivering little girl who he had cheered through the measles only a few weeks ago.

As he continued, calling occasionally for more supplies, the queue seemed to grow ever longer. He washed cuts, bandaged abrasions and put broken arms in slings. He gave comfort to the distressed and encouragement to the brave. Had it been an earthquake, Doctor? He, ·like they, could only surmise. Certainly the loud bang and tremendous shaking which had partially wrecked the top of the house seemed to point to this. He was only glad at this moment that whatever it was had left his surgery virtually intact and his precious medicines unharmed except for a covering of fallen plaster flakes.

When Mrs Ling brought in another patient, and a cup of tea for the doctor, she also gave him the welcome news that Dr Sorby had arrived from his sailing and was going to minister to those injured who were still in the streets. Dr Ling smiled for the first time in quite a while and went back to his work with renewed vigour. Although he did not know it then – though he may well have suspected – he was to be busy right through the rest of the day and well into the night ...

Slowly, now, people were beginning to collect in small groups: some lending their neighbours a hand to salvage items from their wrecked homes, others beginning to clear the debris from the paths and streets. There was much discussion about what had happened, but the general view was that it had been an earthquake. In any event, that was what the rector and Captain Harlow said, and they should know. A few were still afraid there might even be a recurrence.

The place looked, as more than one man who had seen active service, remarked, "as though it had been hit by one of them huge bombs". There didn't seem to be a single house or building which had not been affected to some degree or other. Streets lying in waste and devastation stared the community in the face at every turn.

No one really could quite believe it. For the moment, though they did seem to be safe, and in that they could take a little comfort, putting off thinking for a while the awful cost that they would have to pay, every man, woman and child. Already Dick Ham, the landlord of *The Anchor* was reckoning he could see at least £20,000 worth of damage to the main part of the village alone ...

At the quay, the old ferryman, Jones, who had only just landed on the hard when the earthquake struck, was still sitting dazed in his boat. He had seen the boat sheds roll "like floating corks" and felt the whole quay "on the move – as if going right down".

He spoke quietly now, almost to himself, as if he was unaware that there was anybody listening, "It seemed just like three seas," he said. "And the waves on the river became a great wave on the land which disappeared over the hill who knows where ..."

Until that moment, no one had thought that disaster might also have struck elsewhere.

3 'A Year of Intense Disturbance'

The twelve months preceding the fateful morning of April 22nd 1884 were, in the words of national newspapers and specialist meteorological and scientific journals alike, "a period of intense disturbance on a global scale".

It was a time when the surface of the earth seemed to be particularly beset by the forces of nature: there were freak extremes of weather; volcanoes and earth movements were notably active after years of comparative inactivity; and an epidemic was reported in Europe on a scale unheard of since the Middle Ages. Although, at the time, scientific bodies drew the reports together at their various headquarters, attempts to find an overall pattern and composite picture were not proposed until after the extraordinary chain of events – of which the Great English Earthquake was one – was over.

Was each occurrence a portent to a much later disaster? In hindsight it might be easy to say that they were, but such was the speed with which each new tragedy fell on the heels of the last – at a rate quite unknown before in history and certainly not duplicated since – that it is easy to understand the mounting confusion that must have prevailed in the minds of scientists and layman alike.

In a later chapter in this book we shall examine the particular portents which directly affected the Essex earthquake and pose the question as to why the persistent apprehension shown by numerous people, whether based on 'a feeling' or actual experience, was seemingly ignored. But here, to put the impact of the English devastation more clearly in perspective on a world-wide scale, I think it is important to discuss briefly the natural upheaval taking place everywhere.

Almost a year to the day before the event, the disturbances were presaged in the most dramatic way possible when the volcanic island of Krakatoa in the Sunda Strait of Indonesia, lying between Java and Sumatra, suddenly exploded into life in May 1883. There had been underground rumblings since the previous month, but it was in May that the eruption began in earnest.

The story of the Krakatoa disaster is now too well-known to need more than a brief outline of its occurrence, save to say that the eruptions gained in intensity through June and July, reaching a maximum of devastation on August 26th. The explosion caused widespread destruction in the surrounding area and, coupled with atmospheric phenomena, scattered debris across the Indian Ocean as far as Madagascar.

The eruption continued until October 10th, by which time it had changed irrevocably the geographical shape of the island, overwhelmed large numbers of villages and caused thousands of deaths. It also produced an enormous tidal wave which raced across the Straits, hitting Java and Sumatra, and resulting in the drowning of some 36,000 people.

This disaster, "the most stupendous volcanic outburst of modern times" as it was referred to in contemporary newspaper reports throughout the world, naturally created much interest in Britain, and the populace were among the most generous donors to the relief fund.

The event even found space in the local Essex newspapers whose editors referred to the "luridly picturesque" details of the eruption which had been published, and allowed certain correspondents access to the letters' column with statements that while readers should feel sympathy for the luckless inhabitants they could take comfort from the fact that "England is exempted from the mishaps which befall less favoured lands." This was the British complacency to which I have referred previously in all its naiveté.

Apart from volcanic activity, the previous year had also seen a large increase in the number of earthquakes. In Europe, particularly, such shocks were "very numerous", to quote one report, and a few examples selected at random will serve to illustrate the point.

On March 5th in Cyprus there occurred "the most severe shock experienced for many years", according to the scientific journal, *Nature* (March 22nd). Houses, buildings and stone walls were thrown down, and there was extensive damage at

Limassol. In the following months there were "general seismic disturbances" throughout Southern Europe, in particular great landslips and fissures were recorded at several places in Italy. This particular activity culminated on July 28th with "a terrific report and several minor reports on the island of Ischia", as H.J. Johnston Lavis reports in his *Notices on the Earthquakes of Ischia* (1883). Much damage was caused throughout the island, and Casamicciola and the districts of Tresta, Olivieri, Penella, Casamonte, Mezzavia, most of Lacco, Fango, Monterine and Vajola di Forio were all reduced to ruins. It was estimated that nearly 2,000 lives were lost. The disturbances also continued in August and September.

Throughout the remainder of the year reports of earthquakes of varying degrees were noted from as far apart as the coast of France to the further reaches of Russia, not to mention those coming in from other parts of the world.

In January 1884, there began what the Swiss scientist, Professor August Forel, called the "earthquake period" which lasted for several months and saw occurrences in Switzerland, Austria, France, Spain, Italy and Portugal, and of course Britain herself. There was vast damage to property and buildings and the death total, though never accurately detailed, must have run into hundreds of lives.

While all this activity was being noted in Europe, the same signs were making themselves evident in Britain. Again a handful of examples selected at random underline the point. It has to be said, though, that in the British Isles the shocks were, until that fateful April morning, of a minor character.

On the afternoon of January 16th 1883, there was a shock "accompanied by a rushing sound" in Monmouth, according to *Nature* (January 18th). A slight shock was also reported the same day from the other end of the country at Hastings.

Four months later, shortly after lunch on June 25th, there was a slight disturbance in Devonshire and Cornwall. This was followed just after 2 o'clock by a "shock accompanied by a loud noise". It was felt particularly at Horrabridge, Boscastle, Holsworthy, Hartland, Clovelly, Bude, Princetown, Launceston and Tavistock, and "houses were shaken and crockery rattled", (*Nature* June 28th).

A "slight shock" was recorded on the morning of October 10th at Bournemouth, and while some destruction and slight injury were claimed, this has never been fully substantiated, (*Nature* October 25th).

The shock accompanied by a loud noise which was experienced in Essex on Mersea Island and the surrounding neighbourhood shortly after midnight on February 18th, immediately preceded the Great Earthquake, and as such will be examined in detail later in the book. As a forewarning of what was to follow two months later it could not have been more significant.

In commenting on all this activity, Professor Raphael Meldola, the compiler of the official report on the English earthquake, noted concisely less than a year afterwards, "when with the progress of the science of seismology a complete catalogue of the earthquakes of the world is drawn up, it will be found that the Essex earthquake was one of a group extending over a period of several years, and characterised by exceptional violence in various parts of the world."

But volcanoes and earthquakes were not the only phenomena disturbing the earth's tranquility at this time. The weather, for instance, had been particularly unpredictable through Europe, and by spring 1884, the British Isles had undergone a most unusual winter. According to the authoritative scientific journal, *Symons's Monthly Meteorological Magazine*, it had been the mildest winter for almost a generation – yet extremely wet. The rainfall had been well above the average of most recent winters, being recorded at 8.93 inches against the normal average of 8.74 inches. The number of wet days, in fact, totalled sixty-four and was "the greatest for a quarter of a century," said the publication.

The country had also been lashed by some of the worst storms in living memory. The most dramatic instance being during the night of January 20th when the barometer fell from 30.17 inches to 29.21 inches in four hours, an astonishing fall of 0.96 inches. "It is said," *Symon's Magazine* reported, "to be probably the greatest fall in so short a time yet recorded in the British Isles." The publication also estimated the wind speed during the storm to have been 88 miles per hour – "the highest speed at which the wind has been known to travel in Great Britain." To the people of the nation, from one end to the other, it remained a night of howling gales and devastating rain which would certainly have remained clearly in their minds for many years longer, but for the intervention of the earthquake.

Other perhaps less scientific sources have also alleged that the heavens produced some further startling phenomena at the time of the disaster, including a strange 'red glow' which suffused the sky just before the shock was felt, 'black' rain, and even an eclipse of the sun! However, as these must all be treated as portents because of some of the doubts which surround their reporting, they will be looked at in more detail later on. Particularly fascinating in this respect are the conclusions drawn by the American, Charles Fort, renowed for his unconventional approach to scientific data.

Perhaps, though, the one occurrence which most people in Britain felt might bring imminent tragedy to their doorsteps was the spread of a cholera epidemic throughout Europe.

Not for a great many years had the acute disease of cholera featured in the thoughts of Europeans. Usually found in India and caused by a specific micro-organism (*vibric spirillum*), and characterized by violent diarrhoea, cramps, and high death rate, it was seen as something peculiarly Asiatic. This new outbreak had apparently had its origins in Egypt in 1883 and from there spread rapidly until, by the early part of 1884, it was widespread throughout Southern Europe. Several countries were already counting their death tolls in thousands as doctors fought to contain the epidemic: in Italy the total was 10,000 dead (over half of these being in the stricken city of Naples), in France over 3,000 and Spain was well over the 500 mark.

After such a long absence from Europe, the spread was creating some alarm, not to say panic in certain quarters. *Nature* magazine voiced the scientific attitude, which was not without its own elements of anxiety: "It is a matter of considerable concern, not only on account of the severity of the existing epidemic, but also in connection with the prospects which are in view with respect to the coming year."

Warning voices had already been raised in Britain in official circles and in Parliament, and the entry of all foreigners and returning tourists was being carefully watched at all ports. Rumours abounded that suspected sufferers had been spotted and swiftly placed in quarantine, but the government was anxious to avoid any hysteria and an atmosphere of calm control was strictly observed. So far, after all, the epidemic seemed to have penetrated no further than a few isolated cases in central France, so there was still a long way to go before the British Isles were seriously threatened.

Complacency again? In the absence of concrete evidence, perhaps so and perhaps not. In any event, it was not to prove a vital issue; barely a few weeks after the earthquake fell over England, the epidemic began to retreat, beaten by the skill and dedication of European medical men and women.

So there we have it: Europe and Britain disturbed for nearly a year by a series of the most unusual phenomena. What connection they had with the earthquake of April 22nd in Essex and if other conclusions had been drawn from them, how might things have changed – our examination of the other places where the shock destroyed property and alarmed the inhabitants will help us tell.

4 Britain's Oldest Town Shattered!

Alfred Mason is a cheerful, wiry little man in his ninety-seventh year. Although his eyesight is now failing and he moves slowly, his mind is still very much alert and full of rich memories of nearly a century of Essex life. He lives today in an old peoples' home near Colchester, where he is proud to be the oldest resident, and a life-long bachelor. He is visited regularly by several generations of fond relatives who take him off for little journeys or else to their homes for a day out. In his full and busy life, restricted though it has been from a geographical point of view to one corner of rural Essex, he has witnessed a world changed through two world wars, the introduction of the motor car and the aeroplane as popular means of transport, the coming of the telephone and television, and advances in science and technology which have ultimately carried men to the moon.

He is also one of the few eyewitnesses to the Great English Earthquake who is still alive.

Alfred Mason was born in a small two-roomed cottage at Old Heath near Colchester in August 1878. The son of a market gardener, he came into a tiny rural community dependent to a large degree on the land, although being on the outskirts of Colchester it both traded with, and drew supplies from the borough with its shops, markets and road and rail link to London. Alfred's home was one of a row of cottages standing close to the Bell Inn, where the local men, including his father, liked to meet in the evenings to drink the rich, dark Essex ale, play dominoes and discuss the endless topics of rural gossip. Both the public house and the cottages still exist today, though time has changed them considerably.

The cottages stand on the brow of Old Heath Road which leads down and into the centre of Colchester two miles away; while in the other direction it becomes Rowhedge Road, running on for a mile to the banks of the river Colne opposite Wivenhoe. Then, as now, it was an area of fields and copses, small rivers and the boggy Hythe Marshes – a place of endless fascination for small boys, and one greatly enjoyed by young Alfred who had had a love of nature and the land instilled in him from birth.

In 1884, not yet being able to attend the small village school, Alfred usually began his day by running errands for his mother. The morning of April 22nd was no exception. His account of what happened, which he told me so vividly, came haltingly at first as he attempted to catch every moment of that memorable morning, then swiftly, almost breathlessly, as sights and sounds once so clearly seen by his now almost sightless eyes, flooded back into his memory.

"It was a bright, sunny morning, that Tuesday," he said. "I was sent by mother down the hill to my father's market garden to collect some vegetables for lunch. It was a cauliflower she wanted, we were going to have it for lunch. There were not many people about then, the men were already at work and the women were in their houses.

"I suppose I reached my father's place just a bit after nine. I told him what my mother wanted and he dug up a big cauliflower and gave it to me. He was too busy to talk to me so I set off back up the hill again. I hoped I might see someone to talk to, but there was still no one about.

"I was just in front of *The Bell* when I heard this tremendous rattling noise. The ground also began to shake beneath my feet. I thought I was going to be knocked over and the cauliflower fell out of my hands. The noise was all around me and I was very frightened. I had no idea what it was.

"I just couldn't move and as I stood there I saw slates begin to rattle off the roofs of the houses on both sides of the road. Some of the chimneys were falling as well, and there were big cracks in the walls. It didn't last very long, but the rattling sound was something I'll never forget."

The young Alfred, rooted to the spot, waited with pounding heart to see what would happen next. For a moment there was an awful silence over the place.

"Then people began running out of their houses like a herd of sheep," he recalls. "They were shouting and some were screaming. And there was dust and bits of houses which had fallen everywhere. When I saw these people it seemed to wake me up and I ran to my house, shouting for my mother.

"My younger brother was standing on the porch looking very scared. My mother had just come to the door and was very upset at what had happened. She didn't know what it was. When she looked out and saw what had happened to some of the other places, she said it was a miracle that our house had escaped such damage. There were only some cracks in the walls and plaster off the ceilings. We could see that the roof of *The Bell* was all caved in and there hardly seemed to be a roof with all its tiles on as far as we looked.

"We went out into the street and my mother talked to our neighbours. She heard someone say it must have been an earthquake. Everyone was very upset and some people came out of their houses with cuts and bruises. It was horrifying.

"I remember we didn't have the cauliflower I had brought home for dinner. Everyone was too nervous that the same thing might happen again to think about eating."

In a matter of moments, Alfred Mason had experienced something he would remember all his life: through his years as a young man working on the land, as a farmer at Boxford and into his retirement a generation ago. He has subsequently proved to be one of the last remaining links with the story of the earthquake, and my research was the richer for his memories ...

Colchester is without doubt one of the showpiece towns of Essex. It also boasts the distinction of being 'Britain's Oldest Recorded Town', a claim which is emblazoned on signposts at the entrance to the district. Sited on high ground overlooking the river Colne, it has ancient stone walls still ringing much of the perimeter and giving it a timeless air which only intrusion into its bustling, neon-lit centre can dispel.

The site, so advantageously placed to observe any approach from the Colne (and in turn the North Sea) was first settled by the Ancient Britons. After them came the Romans who turned the 108 acres of the town into an important city, and erected the huge eight-foot thick walls which were to serve as its defence. The town's name under the Romans was *Colonia Camulodunum*, incorporating the name of the nearby river, and it was these industrious conquerors from the south who built the various magnificent archways and gates which can still be seen today in a remarkable state of preservation.

One of these, the Balkern Gate, though undoubtedly of Roman origin, is locally believed to have been part of the castle of 'Old King Cole' the famous nursery rhyme character who is said to have actually reigned in Britain – by courtesy of the Romans – at Colchester around AD 306. Another story maintains that it was from this monarch that the town received its name, and there is a large earthwork, supposed by some to have been a Roman amphitheatre, which is known by the popular name of 'King Cole's Kitchen'.

History has several times proved the advantage of the town's situation and defences, particularly during the Civil War when the population remained loyal to the Stuarts. The walls took a severe battering from Cromwell's artillery before being overrun. After the capture the two leaders, Lucas and Lisle, were mercilessly shot.

The town also has several other splendid ancient buildings, including the remains of St Botolph's Priory Church (founded in 1103), the half-timbered Siege House and the fine castle which occupies nearly twice the area of the White Tower of London. Parts of this were undoubtedly built by the Romans, but the main edifice seems to have been the work of Edward the Elder in 1076, according to Norden's *Survey of Essex*. Today, the castle is a museum which draws visitors from all over the world.

Perhaps not surprisingly, Colchester has become an important garrison town, and army troops from the barracks which are scattered over the southern half of the area have been despatched to the far corners of the earth for many generations now.

Apart from being handily sited for the sea, Colchester is just over fifty miles from London, and for over a century has been regarded as being no more than an easy day's journey from London. Hence it has long attracted trippers and sightseers. Today, a fast train journey can cover the distance in under an hour; motorways following much the same route only take longer because of the ever-increasing number of vehicles on the road.

The local historian, L.B. Stubbs, in his monologue on the

town published at the turn of the century, has admirably summarised its appeal:

> At Colchester there are such immense quantities of Roman bricks to be seen, and other footsteps of that people which evidently show that very great numbers of Roman edifices were formerly standing here. The churches, the Town walls and the castle are half built with Roman materials, and in several parts of them the Roman workmanship is also copied. Roman pavements are still to be found in the town, and a magnificent one is at Mersea, which was most probably the Roman landing place, it being upon a bold open shore and proper for the purpose. To this day, *Camulodunum* (Colchester) still has all the aforementioned marks of ruined grandeur amidst its solid modern prosperity.

The ancient fortified city of the Romans was certainly to need all its strength and durability to withstand the blow which struck it on the morning of April 22nd. As, indeed, was its population of some 28,000 men, women and children.

Colchester was just getting into its morning stride when the clock above the Essex and Suffolk Fire Office in the High Street chimed 9.15 a.m.

The factories throughout the lower part of the town in the Hythe district were hard at work; the shops along the High Street, Head Street and Queen Street were already busy with customers; children were finishing morning assembly and housewives clearing their tables of the breakfast dishes. Several smart black carriages and some farm carts were jogging along the partly cobbled streets, and a few ponies and traps waited patiently beside gas lamps on the pavements. The occasional small group of men and women had already stopped to exchange greetings and small talk outside the business premises, while above them most shutters and windows facing the road had been thrown open to the warm morning sunshine.

At the railway station, situated down North Hill and on the other side of the river Colne, one of the last of the special morning trains to London was preparing to leave. Half a dozen hansom cabs had just brought a number of businessmen into the station yard, and these men were now hastily obtaining their tickets. The stationmaster, Mr W.

Blatch, was already on the platform, flag in hand.

A tall, bearded man, Mr Blatch prided himself on his own punctuality and spared no effort to impose the same standards on trains leaving his station. The train now at the main downline platform consisted of ten carriages and an engine, and formed the 9.20 a.m. express to London, stopping only once at Chelmsford. Mr Blatch looked at the gold fob watch which hung by a chain from his waistcoat pocket. The pride of his father before him, it had always kept immaculate time. It now read 9.18 a.m.

Mr Blatch turned slowly on his heels and looked across the Colne to Colchester standing on its hill. Momentarily, he thought his vision was blurred by a heat haze as everything seemed to rise and sway.

"There was this rumbling noise at the same moment, just like distant thunder," he said, "and directly the platform beneath my feet seemed to heave like the motion of a wave. I felt dizzy in the head and fell back against the wall of the platform."

Before his startled eyes, Mr Blatch watched the engine and carriages of the express rise and fall, the carriages rattling and banging against each other. Windows cracked and glass splintered along the platform and into some of the carriages themselves. Doors sprung open, and the engine driver, who had been standing at the opening to his cab, was pitched out on to the platform. Steam escaped from the engine in an angry squeal.

"Something terrible had obviously happened," Mr Blatch went on, recalling the drama, "and we had received either the shock of an explosion or an earthquake. The passengers on the train all rushed alarmed to the windows of the carriages and some jumped, or fell out, of the doors."

Although the blow seemed to have lasted only "an instant" at the station, there was disarray and panic everywhere. Passengers poured from the compartments, some clutching bruised arms and cut faces. Those who had escaped unhurt were quick to lend assistance to the less fortunate who had been tipped from their seats or actually thrown out of the carriages. Mr Blatch, concerned for his passengers, dropped his flag and hurried to lend assistance. Out of the station building rushed a ticket collector and two porters to give aid. The terrified stoker had also leapt from the cab of the engine to help the driver who lay moaning on the platform.

No trains were to run to or from Colchester for the rest of the day – not until, in fact, the Great Eastern Railway Company had run a heavy engine over all the bridges and thoroughly tested both lines of track to see they were safe for use.

Across the river Colne from the station, what Mr Blatch had mistakenly thought was a heat haze over Colchester was now a huge cloud of dust and crashing debris.

The Essex Telegraph, one of the local papers, printed and published in Colchester, described the first impact on the town with the vividness of personal experience:

Colchester was thrown into a state of indescribable panic and alarm on Tuesday morning by a shock of earthquake. The ground was convulsed from one end of the town to the other, and 'In a moment, in the twinkling of an eye', the occupations and thoughts of scores of thousands of persons were arrested and diverted by the immediate presence of an appalling danger, which threatened to overwhelm the dwellings of rich and poor alike in a common ruin.

It is impossible to exaggerate the feeling of consternation which prevailed. Everybody rushed into the open air, expecting to see visible results of the subterranean commotion and to be able instantaneously to divine the cause. Women shrieked in their terror and alarm in the most piercing manner, and strong men seemed utterly helpless to console them, being themselves completely unnerved and paralysed.

The revelations made in the succeeding minutes of what had actually happened only intensified the panic ...

Dr Alexander Wallace, one of Colchester's leading citizens and a well-known local physician, was close to one of the worst scenes of devastation in the small back street of Lion Walk. Here half the massive spire of the Lion Walk Congregational Church was shaken down and plunged partly into the church itself and the remainder into the road.

From his home at Trinity House, Dr Wallace was to provide a full and carefully detailed report of what happened:

I was indoors, seated, reading my newspaper, and not conscious of any shock, but only of a great noise and shaking of the floors and ceiling above, the rattling of windows, ringing of bells, with a noise of artillery, and then the crash of falling masonry. Exclaiming, 'An earthquake!' I rushed out of doors with my family.

Those adults of my family who were standing in my garden, occupying and having a view over an acre of ground or more, testified that the first thing noticeable was a low rumbling, proceeding from the earth, not from above; a rolling sound indescribable, unlike anything else, coming to them from a distance in the south-west, passing under them, and proceeding in the north-east direction; next a vibratory rocking, felt chiefly at the knees, causing unsteadiness, and attempts to lay hold on surrounding objects which only made them feel more unsteady. At the same time surrounding objects, buildings etc., seemed to be rocking and swaying.

The next they observed were the falling chimneys around and the crumbling and fall of the spire of the Congregational Chapel close by. It was clearly noticed that the fall of chimneys to the south-west of them preceded the fall of the spire, which is to the east of us; in fact they fell one after another; those furthest to the south-west fell first. Moreover, the debris of the spire and of the chimneys nearly all over Colchester has tumbled on the north and north east sides of the buildings, and many of the cracks are lower on the north side than on the south, pointing to the conclusion that in addition to a mere vibration something like a wave of upheaval was felt approaching from the south-west, and causing a fall in the opposite direction.

Dr Wallace's testimony proved to be one of the most important pieces of substantive evidence about the 'wave' effect of the earthquake. It lacked, though, the emotion felt by most eyewitnesses to the devastation.

Like young Herbert Johnson, the ten-year-old son of Mr Herbert Johnson senior, a plumber, who lived in Lion Walk almost immediately opposite the Congregational Church. He was actually standing at the door of his home, one of a row of two-storey red-bricked houses, when the quake struck.

"Everything shook and bounced about," he said, "and there was a great rumbling noise. Then the spire on the church seemed to shake apart and came crashing down all over the place."

The small, terrified boy stood unable to move as the

TERRIBLE EARTHQUAKE IN ESSEX.

Great Alarm & Damage to Property at Colchester.

LANGENHOE CHURCH DESTROYED

Wyvenhoe, Mersea, and other Parishes Wrecked.

Not within living memory has Colchester been thrown into such a state of excitement, consternation, and panic, as it was soon after nine o'clock on Tuesday morning, when the town was visited by a fearful and most appalling earthquake, which will remain in the recollection of those who experienced it to their dying day. Everything was peaceful and quiet early on in the morning, no fresh atmospherical change from the last few days, with the exception of a slight elevation of temperature, being experienced to indicate in any way the approach of a visitation of this nature, from which England happily has been very free, and has had little or no cause to anticipate anything of the kind either in years gone by or at this more immediate period. The awful event occurred between a quarter and twenty minutes past nine o'clock, coming without the slightest warning, and lasting from five to ten seconds, but in that short period of time, an amount of damage was done to property which it will take weeks to set right, and in some cases the destruction is irreparable. From one end of the town to the other the ground was convulsed, and if a spectator could have taken a bird's eye view of the Borough, the effect would have been much the same as a sea wave, the ground upheaving and lowering by means of that gigantic power pent up beneath the earth's crust. The general impression appears to be that the ground and the houses with it was lifted up, shaken two or three times in a manner that made the stoutest heart quake, and the bravest to cow with fear, and then subside, disappearing with a kind of final shake or jerk, and then all was over. No noise like the rumbling sound of artillery in the distance, no crash similar to that of a thunderbolt, or the roaring of the boiling ocean, as one expects to hear accompanying a shock of this nature, but there was simply a sort of low rumbling sound, caused as it were more by the creaking and shaking of the houses than anything else. Not a house in the Borough escaped its mighty influence, clocks stopped, bells were set a-ringing, furniture displaced, pictures dislodged from the walls, vases and ornaments overturned, and no end of damage of a more serious character was done in the space of a few seconds.

A headline story from *The Essex Standard*

masonry crashed down, huge chunks bouncing up from the road against the houses. Pieces flew around Herbert, missing him only by inches, and one large section actually coming to rest by his feet. At this, he at last turned and fled in panic into the house.

A large proportion of the spire fell clear of the church and into the graveyard, demolishing the tombstones and converting the whole enclosure into a wreck. Other portions fell on to the roof above the North aisle of the church, and crashed through into the main body of the building, some heavier pieces even breaking into the basement. As *The Essex Telegraph* summarized, "The whole fabric was shattered to the basement. The effect of the shock seems to have been to lift the tower bodily on its southern side, and there is now a distinct inclination to the north of the rent and fissured building. Many of the stones at the point of detachment threatened at any moment to overwhelm any passing pedestrian."

The destruction of the church proved to be the second of two terrible blows to the congregation. For not only was the spire a replacement for an earlier edifice which had been blown down by a storm, but only the previous week, the man who had been responsible for the building of the church and ministered to its people for many years, the Reverend T.W. Davids, had died. We shall look again at this sad coincidence later in the book.

As the people of Colchester took to the debris-covered streets, rumours about the reason for the disturbance sped from person to person. The first, and most popular, story was that the gas works near the Hythe Docks had exploded or been deliberately destroyed.

The docks, used by huge barges coming up the Colne from the North Sea, bringing timber, coal and grain from ports around the coast of the British Isles, were particularly busy on this morning, and dockers swarmed over several of the vessels. They fell, tumbling and shouting, in a flurry of cascading sacks and overturned planks, when the shock rippled across the area.

At the East Mill, sacks also toppled over on workmen, and those who were actually on the barges felt them rock violently. A team of men working on a barge belonging to Messrs

Marriage and Sons, which was on its way from the Hythe, to the company's flour mills just up river, felt it "lifted up and dropped again" in the water. These same men also saw a "huge wave pass across the meadows lying between East Bridge and the Tendring Hundred Railway."

The extensive engineering works of Messrs Davey, Paxman and Co on Hythe Hill was considerably shaken by the blow. Several of the huge roof supports were nearly dragged from their fittings and horrified workers ran into the streets. There was a particularly narrow escape for one gang of workmen when a huge wooden girder, about sixteen feet long, toppled over beside them.

There was a hairsbreadth escape, too, for some drain diggers at work in a trench in Factory Lane. The oscillating ground tipped pipes and earth into the trench on top of several men, and one was trapped by falling planks. On being rescued the man was found to be suffering from a broken arm.

When the initial terror passed, however, it was to the gas works that all eyes turned. Dust and debris seemed to surround the buildings, and men could be seen hurrying out, some supporting injured colleagues.

The Essex Herald, another local paper, described what happened: "The large gasometers were seen to rock, bricks fell from the neighbouring buildings, and naturally the first thought to occur to those in responsible positions was that the place had been blown up or an attempt had been made to wreck it."

To the bewildered people in the streets, their worst fears seemed to be confirmed when the Deputy Mayor, Mr J.B. Harvey, and the Superintendent of Police, Mr R.D. Coombs, were later seen hurrying to the works in a cab. They were soon joined by the Chairman of the Directors of the Gas Company and a force of several police constables.

"It soon became evident, however, that this could not be the cause," *The Essex Herald* went on, "as there was no eruption of the ground where the mains were laid, and the gas would still light when a match was applied to the burners."

The arrival of the police did prove timely, nonetheless, for a huge crowd of people had soon gathered outside the gas works, and the men in blue were needed to hold them back and endeavour to calm their fears.

The army camp and barracks on the opposite side of the town also featured in the wildfire rumours. Because of the large amount of ammunition and powder stored within the precincts of the garrison, reports were soon claiming that the area had been laid waste by this material blowing up. *The Essex Standard* elaborated on this particular story: "Perhaps it originated in the fact that the greatest alarm was manifested in the Camp and Barracks, where a considerable amount of damage was done, and also that a Battery of Artillery, which was driving across the Abbey Field, seemed to completely lose their heads, some standing still, whilst others ran as fast as they could from their guns, fancying no doubt that the shock had something to do with atmospheric electricity, and that the further they were from their guns the better for themselves.

A variation on this story had it that the garrison had been blown up by the notorious Dynamiters who were then causing considerable upheaval in the major cities of England. However, as evidence suggests this was a much more prevalent rumour in Chelmsford, it will be dealt with in that later section.

Colchester had, by now, come to a standstill. As *The Illustrated Police News* – which commissioned the evocative drawings reproduced elsewhere in the book – stated, "Business was suspended at once, schools and factories were immediately closed, and crowds of persons filled the streets to inspect the damage. In all directions fallen chimneys and portions of buildings were visible, and for some time one was in considerable danger in walking through the streets."

The first group of people to get an idea of the extent and amount of the devastation was probably the Essex and Suffolk Fire Brigade, a group of volunteer firemen who raced breathlessly from their headquarters in the High Street to several fires, and from one area of devastation to the next. They sped from Maidenburgh Street to Roman Road and East Hill, extinguishing flames and helping rescue several old people trapped in their homes.

As reports from the various districts of the town were drawn together, it soon became clear that the greatest amount of destruction had been suffered in the lower parts of Colchester towards the Hythe, especially along East Hill, Brook Street, Magdalen Street and Barrack Street. This was the oldest part of the town, and several of its narrow streets were crowded with tenaments and old cottages. Roofs had been untiled, chimneys thrown down, and debris scattered in the roads and in many of the houses themselves. People both indoors and out had been knocked over, and not a few struck by falling plaster and bricks.

St Leonard's Church in the Hythe had, like the Lion Walk Congregational Church, lost its spire during the shock, and this badly damaged both the church and the rectory. Dr Manning, the Rector, who had been preparing to leave his house, narrowly escaped death when two stacks fell from the rectory roof and plunged through the upstairs rooms and into the sitting room where he was standing.

Although St Leonard's was badly damaged and surrounded by debris, the manual fire engine which was stored in the nave for use in case of emergencies was virtually unscratched. Under the guidance of Mr Isaac Martin, who served as fireman, watchman, and sexton in the Hythe district, the engine was hauled out and put to rescue work. Mr Martin had recruited volunteers to his 'force' as he ran to the church from his home on Hythe Hill, carrying over his shoulder the huge church door key which was fifteen inches long and weighed six pounds!

One of the strangest stories concerning this area was related in *The Essex Standard* of a young lady who was walking in Sheep's Head Meadow, at the rear of the castle. "She experienced no sensation of the earth moving," the newspaper reported, "but saw to her astonishment and consternation a cottage in Maidenburgh Street topple over and become a partial wreck without any apparent cause."

At the castle the shock was "severely felt". The curator of the building and its museum, Mr Gunner, reported that many items on display had been knocked over or damaged. Many objects were moved in their cases, and a Roman soldier's bronze helmet – shaped like a jockey's peaked cap – which stood in a recess cut in a twelve-foot-thick wall was turned completely round.

Colchester   High   Street   had   been   the   scene   of unprecedented panic and fear: people had been bowled over, horses had shied and run amok, and the bricks and masonry which had tumbled from shop roofs had thrown up dust and confusion like a bombardment.

Mr J.B. Harvey, the Deputy Mayor, who had a shop adjoining the Public Hall, found himself one of the busiest men in the borough, rushing from one trouble spot to another. He recorded his emotions the following day: "The feeling was of a nature one does not wish to experience for a second time – a sickening, unnerving sensation, augmented by the necessary attendant of the vibrations, the violent ringing of bells, the smashing of glass and the crashing of falling chimneys and buildings."

Mr Harvey said the noise of the earthquake increased in intensity and sounded like "a locomotive passing through the premises and shaking the house and offices and also the Public Hall adjoining to their foundations." He could distinctly hear the screams of fear and panic from the street.

In the Town Hall, the hall keeper underwent a frightening experience. *The Essex Standard* reports, "The Keeper was in the large room at the time of the shock, and he states that the whole structure shook fearfully from top to bottom. He ran against the wall near the fire-place apprehending the roof was falling, but with the exception of some plaster from the ceiling and a portion of the stone coping at one corner of the exterior which was detached and fell on the pavement, no damage was done."

No doubt the huge solidarity of the stone building accounted for its lack of damage, but the movement of the walls apparently gave several people inside the feeling that they were being attacked by a fit. This was particularly true of the elderly Town Clerk, Mr F.B. Philbrick who, according to *The Essex Telegraph*, "was thus affected, and thought he should fall on the floor insensible; but he recovered the moment the wave had passed."

At the back of the High Street, in Culver Street, quick thinking also averted a disaster at the Wesleyan School. The shock tipped many of the children from their benches, and in panic they began scrambling for the doors as plaster and debris showered from the ceilings.

Although the Head Master, Mr H.E. Shaw, and his assistants were much alarmed by what happened, they swiftly put into operation the fire drill they had so often rehearsed, calming the children and filing them quickly from the building. A check among the bewildered youngsters, several of whom were crying, revealed that only a few had actually been injured and required treatment. In common with the other schools in the district, the Wesleyan children were immediately sent home for the rest of the day.

Just off Culver Street, in the curiously named Short Wire Street, Mr W.C. Aberdein had been serving the last few morning breakfasts in his 'Commercial Cafe' when he heard and felt the shock. As an ex-sailor, Mr Aberdein naturally compared the sensation to his naval experience: "It sounded like the discharge of a 68 pound gun on the upper deck as felt in the lower deck of a ship." The walls of the cafe shook and buckled, plates and food were flung from the tables and customers pitched on to the floor. Mr Aberdein, who was in his kitchen at the time, was thrown against the door leading into the dining room.

"My first idea was that my premises fronting the street were falling. Knowing that my wife and two of my daughters were in the bedrooms, I rushed upstairs, and met them at the top, screaming. One of them said that the house was falling.

"Well they might, for four feet of the centre stack of four flues fell crashing through the roof, and part of the debris, falling through the chimneys of the two bedrooms, almost overtook them in their exit," he said.

In fact, the masonry crashed through the ceilings into the ground floor dining room, bursting on to the tables and customers below.

"A gentleman having his breakfast laid hold of the waitress, dragged her some distance, and exclaiming, 'We shall all be killed', rushed out of the house, and we have not seen him since!" added Mr Aberdein.

Coincidentally, in the light of the panic-stricken man's words, it was in Long Wire Street that the most serious accident caused by the earthquake in Colchester occurred. Mr Aberdein himself heard the story of a Mrs Doe who ran from her home and was felled by falling debris, but did not record the extent of her injuries in his statement.

According to reports, Mrs Doe, who lived at number 14, was struck by a large piece of chimney stack and suffered serious head injuries. She was rushed to the Essex and Colchester Hospital and put under intensive care for several days. Conflicting stories say she hovered close to death for twenty-four hours before beginning to recover, while one persistent rumour actually maintained she had died.

Mrs Doe's accident is dramatically recorded in the reconstruction of the earthquake drawn for *The Illustrated Police News* which is reprinted elsewhere in this book – although her name is incorrectly given as Dove and her address as Magdalen Street!

It is perhaps not surprising to find that the High Street area is the focus of the most detailed reports – the newspapers being well aware how familiar it was to people throughout Essex and even further afield: viz these paragraphs from *The Essex Standard*:

> Go where one would, the fearful result of the devastation met the eye, the ground being here and there strewn with heaps of debris, the remains of stacks of chimneys, slates, and other things, which had all met with a similar fate at the hands of the sweeping power.
>
> The large block of buildings at Head Gate, known as the Auction Rooms, and occupied by Mr C. Fuller, were so shaken as to cause a fissure between that building and the adjacent one, the 'Elephant and Castle Inn'.
>
> A stack of chimneys at Mr R.J. Halls, fishmonger, High Street, was demolished and fell into the yard, where some men were at work; and Mr Halls' man, Munson, was near, and although not hurt, he received such a shock that he was quite helpless for some time and had to be led home.
>
> The 'Marquis of Granby' inn on North Hill, along with several other of the town's public houses, was badly damaged, particularly by stacks falling through the roof. Many glasses were broken and much beer lost.
>
> The old buildings in Schere Gate were rent, and a tall chimney, which is only to be seen from St John Street, was shattered to such an extent that the public were prevented from using the steps until the damage had been sufficiently repaired as to ensure safety.

The several Churches of Colchester were all seen to shake and move and most were extensively damaged. The wild ringing of their bells only added to the terror of the moment.

The Workhouse, which is very substantially built, has also suffered, three chimneys being totally wrecked, which crashed through the roof and caused the greatest consternation and excitement among the inmates.

The premises in Osborne Street, used by the Young Woman's Help Society, have been partly demolished by the falling down of two of their chimneys, and the adjacent premises, occupied by Mr Stone, were fissured by the shock.

St Martin's Club, in West Stockwell Street, showed signs of the severity of the shock; whilst the Conservative Club also suffered. Fortunately few members were yet in attendance at either, or serious injury might have been sustained.

Messrs W. and R. Cheshire, glass and china shop in St Botolph's Street, felt the shock very severely, a large quantity of glass and china being knocked off the shelves, the amount of damage being estimated at over £10. Three Army medical officers who dashed into the street in this vicinity caused considerable consternation as they were only partially dressed!

And so on – drama and damage everywhere.* The paper could not close its list, however, without mention of its own incident: "A large chimney on the back premises of Mr Brewers, hosier, High Street, fell with great force upon the roof of the printing office of *The Essex Standard*, adjacent, where a number of hands were at work; but the roof happily withstood the shock, although damage was done."

The area was not without its intensely human stories, too – little incidents which might have been lost forever, but for the kindness of people passing them on for inclusion in this book. I have selected three items, no doubt typical of hundreds of

---

* Commenting in more general terms on the town as a whole, *The East Anglian Daily Times* said, "In Colchester the extent of the damage is appalling. The loss of property is prodigeous. Not only are innumerable roofs wrecked, but the falling debris in hundreds of instances injured other portions of the houses. Besides, crockery was thrown down in all directions; in shops and warehouses stock-in-trade was broken and windows smashed. The amount of destruction is absolutely beyond computation. In Colchester alone it has been guessed at, it is impossible to compute it – as high as £200,000." Although many of the estimates of damage at the time erred on the side of caution, this one was certainly over-generous as we shall see later in the book!

similar experiences, and two of which are particularly valuable in that they happened to people still alive today. The first concerns a Mr T.J. Moore of Providence Place, whose story was sent to me by an old Colchester resident, and had been clipped from *The Essex Telegraph* of April 26th 1884. Mr Moore writes,

Sitting by the fire, and almost set fast with rheumatism, I was alarmed by my wife running downstairs, shrieking. Thinking she was falling down, and forgetting for the moment the pain I was suffering, I sprang to her assistance, and fortunate for me I did so, for at that moment a number of bricks came down the chimney, smashing the teapot and the top of the stove, and hurling a kettle of boiling water into the very spot I had then vacated, and the room was instantly filled with soot and debris. We were severely shaken, but no further damage was done.

In one of the strange, isolated spots where the upheaval passed with only a minimum of effect was Miss L. Ranson, who was spending the day with her grandparents, the owners of a small grocer's shop in East Stockwell Street. She was just about four years old at the time and found the shop an absolute Aladdin's cave of delights – and temptation, as she recalled recently in St Mary's Hospital in Colchester where she has been a patient for the last two years.

Just prior to the shock, the little girl had crept into the shop as there were no customers and her grandmother was outside. The particular attraction were two drawers containing brown and white sugar lumps. She had just opened one drawer and was taking a surreptitious pinch when the shock caused the building to tremble and the bell over the door to ring.

The movement and the ringing of the bell naturally brought Miss Ranson's grandmother hurrying into the shop, half expecting to find a customer, and instead a small, frightened child caught with her hand in the sugar drawer!

Mrs M.K. Bird, who now lives in Ipswich, was also a small child of four years old when the earthquake shook the town. She lived with her parents at Prospect Cottage at the top of North Hill and recalls the day clearly.

"I can remember sitting in our room and the whole house began shaking. My father rushed out to see what had happened and there were tiles and debris falling everywhere.

"After it was all still again, we went down to my Grandmother Godfrey's house at the bottom of North Hill. We thought it would be safer there because the chimneys on our house were not safe and might fall. We only went back later when the builders had secured everything," she said.

At the rear of the Birds' cottage stood an enormous water tower sited on the highest part of the town at Balkerne Hill. This structure, some 140 feet high, supported a tank capable of holding a quarter of a million gallons of water and provided the town with its water supply. Because of its size and its dominant position – it was visible from several miles away – the tank had become known to young and old alike as 'Jumbo'. On the morning of April 22nd, 'Jumbo' was a focal point of many people's attention.

"When the trembling came, the tower bagan to move from side to side," one anonymous resident who had been walking down the High Street towards North Hill told *The Essex Telegraph*. "I staggered against the side of a shop, but I couldn't keep my eyes off 'Jumbo'.

"It seemed to sway several times on its legs, and I thought what a terrible disaster there would be if it fell over on to the cottages. By a miracle it righted itself as soon as the shock passed. If the earthquake had gone on a moment longer I'm sure it would have fallen," he said.

That the tower withstood the blow proved to be a vindication of the views of its designer, Sir Henry Rawlinson, who had spoken emphatically on its stability when, earlier, doubts had been raised about the likelihood of it falling in a heavy storm or some similar freak of nature. During the course of the day many people came to inspect the tank, a great many of them having been convinced it would fall under the blow.

Another focal point of the crowds who took to the streets was the Post Office, not far from the tower, in Head Street.

In 1884, the telephone was still a novelty, and the telegraph the only really satisfactory means of communication with the outside world. Had the earthquake struck elsewhere? That was the question the people who beseiged the Post Office wanted to know. *The Essex Telegraph* takes up the story:

At the time of the shock, the officials on the ground floor and the telegraphic staff upstairs were pursuing their usual duties when the building seemed to sway. The greatest alarm prevailed, and the whole of those who were on the upper floors rushed down into the street, under the impression that the building, which is very high and contains more floors than any other house in the borough, was about to collapse.

Finding on reaching the open air that their experience was by no means peculiar to themselves, they returned and found to their astonishment that the telegraphic wires appeared to be intact although the walls and ceilings were badly cracked.

The Chief Clerk, Mr Aldis, made a swift examination of the building and was similarly amazed that the communications system had survived the quake. Soon the first bewildered and frightened local people were arriving at the office for information and to send messages.

Mr Aldis organized his staff quickly and efficiently. "The necessities of the public compelled the officials at once to resume their duties," he reported later, "and for a long period the four wires to London were kept constantly occupied, about 1,000 messages being dealt with during the day. Some 8,000 words were despatched as Press messages to the London and provincial papers describing the occurrence. There was in fact no cessation in the stream of messages from about ten in the morning until four in the afternoon."

Later in the day the postal department underwent a similar rush when letters and parcels containing the first newspaper reports were hurried into the mails. Said the Post Office, "The influx of letters in reply during Wednesday, Thursday and Friday, extra to the usual traffic, has been numbered by tens of thousands."

Telegrams, by way of the Post Office, also brought the first news reports of the extent of the earthquake from the Press Association in London. Rumours of wholesale death and destruction, particularly in London, where it was said that Liverpool Street Station had been wrecked and the Monument fallen, were widespread throughout the town, and it was not until midday that the P.A. supplied the waiting population of Colchester with their first news – incorrect as it subsequently proved to be: "Earthquake appears to have been purely local, as we have heard only from Colchester and

Ipswich. Nothing felt in London."

At 1.28 p.m. the Press Association revised this statement with a second telegram: "Later enquiries show that shock was felt in London, about same hour as at Ipswich, and caused for time much alarm."

Just over an hour later at 2.47 p.m. the picture of a major earthquake having occurred was slowly but surely taking shape: "Earthquake was distinctly felt in London today. Telegraphic instruments were affected, and in large establishments walls rocked causing much alarm to employees, who rushed into streets. Shock was also experienced at Chelmsford, Maldon, Shoeburyness, and Southend. Later telegrams from Ipswich and Colchester state that more damage was done than at first expected."

By the middle of the afternoon, special editions of the local newspapers carrying the first sketchy reports were appearing on the streets, and being literally snapped up by the population. Queues formed outside the newspaper offices – often stretching for a hundred yards and more – and printing presses "could barely keep pace with the demand for copies," according to *The Essex Standard.*

As night fell, the people of Colchester began to realize that their experience had probably also been shared by millions of other people throughout Southern England. Not until the following days, though, were they to learn to just what extent.

The Times gave the first broad hint in its report on the next morning, April 23rd: "Up to a late hour details were pouring in of the devastation caused by the earthquake in the many villages in the neighbourhood from Colchester to the sea. The wreckage which meets the eye on every side is heart-rending, especially as most of the damage is done to tenaments occupied by poor persons, many of whom are now completely homeless."

5 'Mersea Island Wrecked'

For their first editions after the morning of April 22nd, the local papers of Essex picked, almost without exception, a single dramatic headline for special prominence on their front pages:

MERSEA ISLAND WRECKED!

Not that this was considered the most important facet of the earthquake story – the papers were indeed full of reports and despatches from all over Southern England, a good many perhaps far more interesting and unusual – but somehow the devastation of this beauty spot just off the Essex coast and flanked by the estuaries of the Colne and Blackwater, typified what had happened throughout the entire district. And being an island, it had an added relevance to the country as a whole.

To this day, that headline remains a legend on the island, while the details themselves are mostly completely forgotten, or confined to the dust-laden files of long defunct newspapers.

Mersea Island, settled on and used by fishermen and small farmers since before the Roman invasion of Britain, is divided into two sections, West and East Mersea – the former being the main area of habitation and a suitable landing spot for sea craft, the latter flat and windswept, and facing treacherous, grey mudflats. A single road running across the causeway from the mainland – built by the Romans – and splitting in two directions immediately on reaching solid ground serves the island which is five miles long by two miles wide.

Mersea's recorded history began with the Romans who utilised it at the time of their creation of Colchester – just inland up the river Colne – as a mighty walled city. They called it *Meressaia*, 'The Isle of the Sea', and apart from establishing a military post and anchorage for their war galleys, regarded it as one of the healthiest places in England, to which they sent injured and exhausted soldiers to recuperate.

Long after the Romans had left their shores, the people of Mersea showed themselves to be just as independent and sturdy, and from their ranks were to come smugglers, pirates, privateers and even great men-of-war sailors, many of whose descendants still ply the waters today, fishing and dredging for oysters. The whole island is legend-haunted with tales of smuggling, witchcraft, and perhaps more ghost stories per square mile than any equivalent district in the British Isles.

On the morning of April 22nd, most of the local fishermen of the 1,300 population were already at work at the fateful moment. Those who were close to the island heard the 'loud rumbling sound' of the earthquake before a huge wave swept across their bows, driving most of the boats backwards in the sea and capsizing several dinghies. Vessels that were anchored were buffeted against their moorings, several suffered damage to their hulls, and at least three men were tipped overboard.

Mr Larman, the island's chief coastguard, was on the quay at West Mersea, and saw the ground beneath his feet move in a wave motion almost simultaneously with the disturbance at sea. *The White Hart* public house just behind him trembled violently and he saw it "apparently lifted bodily up and the four chimneys on the roof thrown down".

But it was inland that Mersea experienced the most terrifying effects; effects that subsequently proved to be unique throughout the whole 150 square miles of disturbance.

On the slightly higher hinterland, the ground groaned and moved under the stresses of the earthquake – then suddenly split and opened in several places. These cracks and fissures ran like quicksilver through fields and gardens alike, some extending for over a hundred yards, others being little more than a few feet long. Most opened only a few inches, but one or two gaped "like the very jaws of hell", as one eyewitness described.

The worst fissure was one extending for nearly 150 yards on the slope near Mersea Lane and running down St Peter's Well on the West Mersea foreshore (see photograph reproduced elsewhere in the book). This well, which had provided the islanders with their fresh water for generations, was actually being used at the moment of impact by an old fisherman.

"The earth just gaped open with a loud sort of noise," he

said later, "and it threw me on the ground. The crack was quite wide and my arm slipped in it. I suppose it was about a foot wide and at least two yards deep. A small fellow could have fallen in it quite easily." The old salt was naturally shaken by the occurrence, but hastily dragged himself to his feet when water began to spray over him. The fissure had caused the water, which normally drained down into the well, to be forced out in a jet.

Water sprays like these were to be observed at several other fissures which appeared on the island, including two at Cross Farm, which broke out in a hundred-foot-long crack and lasted for almost nine hours. A Mr Edward Newton who visited the farm said, "They were about ten yards apart and a woman who lived in the house close by informed me that there was enough water to cause a small stream to run down from each place to her house, where they formed a pond."

Observers recorded, too, that all these water spouts were white in colour, as if mixed with lime, and were quite warm. None of them resumed their usual condition until the following day.

The picture of devastation which was found throughout the island pointed to West Mersea having been more badly hit than the eastern sector, and the quite remarkable fact that here wooden buildings had withstood the quake better than brick ones.

After the subsidence of the initial panic which had sent men, women and children fleeing from their homes in a hail of falling debris, taking stock of the situation showed that quite a considerable percentage of the population were going to be homeless for a time. A telegram from the occupants of two cottages at West Mersea to their landlord, a Mr Sales of Galleywood, near Chelmsford, speaks more graphically than a thousand words of the common plight: BOTH COTTAGES WRECKED. WE ARE OUT IN THE STREETS. WHAT SHALL WE DO? CAN YOU COME?

The greatest drama, though, had undoubtedly been at the Parish School where, but for the presence of mind of the schoolmaster, the earthquake might well have taken a terrible death toll. Several graphic accounts of this event have survived, and I reproduce one from *The Essex Telegraph* which seems to capture the whole incident most dramatically. It also underlines the comments of the *Telegraph*'s contemporary, *The Essex Standard* that "it is marvellous that there was not some loss of life or personal injury."

About 140 children of both sexes, and ages varying from three to thirteen, were assembled when the shock was felt. Some sixty of these were having a scripture lesson in the infant school, an apartment adjoining the main building, and into which a portion of the wall and roof fell, close alongside the raised tier of seats on which the little ones were.

In an instant the place was full of dust and soot, and, as might be expected, something approaching panic took place. The children screamed and rushed towards the door. Mr John Thorpe, the schoolmaster, not knowing what had really happened, but realising that there was some terrible danger, got to the door instantly, and threw it open, only to find a shower of tiles and bricks descending from the roof.

The children came tumbling one over another towards him, but with one arm he snatched up a little girl of three who had fallen, and, standing in the doorway, was able to use his other to check the rush, the young ones calming down when they found him amongst them. In a minute or two, when the rain of bricks had ceased, he allowed the school to disperse.

Mr Thorpe later informed us that notwithstanding the alarming position in which he found himself his efforts were directed to a prevention of such calamities as those of Newcastle, where the children were suffocated in their attempts to rush disorderly from a building on the occasion of an alarm.

By one of those strange coincidences that seem to dot the story of the earthquake, Mr Thorpe had actually carried out a fire drill only the previous day, and although the younger children panicked, it was still fresh enough in the minds of the older pupils for them to put it into effect with complete success. Mr Thorpe's own house adjoining the school was similarly badly cracked and one entire wall collapsed; fortunately no one was on the premises at the time.

West Mersea Church was also damaged, the belfry being cracked and a great many tiles displaced. The chimneys on the rectory nearby fell in, completely unroofing the building, and greatly alarming the inhabitants, including the Vicar, the Reverend Thomas Musselwhite.

Later in the week the Reverend Musselwhite contributed his impressions of the earthquake in an interview with *The Essex Standard*:

> The shock was felt here very severely. The direction of the earth wave seemed to be from north-east to south-west. It was accompanied by a loud rumbling sound, a strong sound which only lasted a few seconds.
>
> There are few chimneys which remain standing; some have been broken at their juncture with the roofs, and after being bent and twisted, have fallen back into nearly their former positions. Indeed, all our buildings are now fearfully shattered; how we shall restore our pretty island I cannot tell.

The despair in Reverend Musselwhite's letter is evident in every line; a despair felt by so many other people in Essex. We shall be returning to this gentleman again later to discuss the strange premonition he had about the earthquake ...

Back along the river Colne from Mersea, and standing on the opposite bank to Wivenhoe, were the two small communities of Fingringhoe and Langenhoe which also featured extensively in the first reports of the earthquake as the destruction they suffered appeared typical of that in numerous small Essex villages.

Photographs taken here of the damage were to prove perhaps more effective in convincing the nation of the extent of what had actually happened than the many thousands of words written about it. Undoubtedly, the picturesque rural scenery of the district provided a most telling background to the ruined cottages and smashed buildings – thereby offering great scope to the skilful photographer.

The Parish Church of Langenhoe attracted the greatest attention, doubtless because of its romantic. history and the terrible damage it suffered. The ancient, ivy-clad stone building stood overlooking the creeks of the river Colne where the Danish Vikings were said to have landed for their raids on English countryside. The church, believed to date at least from Norman times, and dedicated to St Andrew, had stood sentinel while the rich flood of Essex history had passed by, and formed part of the estate which had had for owners Earl Eustace, the Fitzwalter family, the Petres, the Waldgraves and, in 1884, the Lord Lieutenant of Essex, Lord Carlingford.

By the nineteenth century, the church had acquired a new element of fame, as *The Essex Telegraph* remarked, "The edifice has long presented the leading peculiarity of the historic erection at Pisa: it has a leaning tower – not so built, but so grown from age and bad foundations." Although this feature proved an attraction to visitors, it was also a source of anxiety to the Rector, the Reverend W. Parkinson, who had been voicing his fears for some time in an effort to raise funds for the building's restoration. For him, the earthquake proved almost a blessing in disguise.

On the morning of April 22nd, Reverend Parkinson was at work in his study at the rectory, close by the church, when he experienced "a violent shock".

"The room in which I was seemed to be lifted up," he said later. "Several persons in the house, including myself, were thrown to the ground. The chimneys were shattered and part of the roof collapsed. The walls and ceilings were cracked, furniture was moved, crockery was shaken from the shelves and bottles were thrown down in the cellar." (He was to find on later inspection that the whole building had been so badly strained as to make it impossible to open or shut any of the doors.)

When the rector emerged shaken, but unhurt, from his home, he saw that the church had suffered far more severely.

"It seemed utterly ruined," he recalled thinking as he hurried across the churchyard. "I could see that some tons of the stone battlements of the tower had been dislodged. These had fallen with great force upon the nave, which was almost entirely destroyed. Debris had also fallen upon the small gallery, fireplace and pews, and the result was a complete wreck of those parts of the building.

"Besides this, the chancel roof was stripped of its tiling, and the stone coping over the window had crashed down, stripping off the branches of a laburnum tree growing nearby. The walls of the chancel and nave were visibly cracked in several places as was the porch."

The rector went into the building through the porch, which was a comparatively recent addition to the structure, and in his eyes "wretchedly ugly at the best of times". Through the settling dust and still groaning beams, he saw terrible devastation – and half the roof open to the sky.

"Inside the scene of wreckage beggered description, and can only be imperfectly appreciated by viewing the photographs taken afterwards," he said. "Roof timbers and masonry had smashed the pews and pulpit. The altar was buried under debris and the choir gallery had been ripped from its wall foundations."

As Reverend Parkinson walked bewildered through the wreckage, he looked up again at the stone tower and saw that its leaning appearance was now even more pronounced. He could come to no other conclusion than that the building had been struck by an earthquake: for a horrifying moment he thought of the carnage and death that would have resulted if the day had been a Sunday.

Bricks, glass and splintered timber also littered the churchyard, which had been fissured in several places, and in the tiny vestry gowns and communion furniture had been thrown on to the floor. Back in the nave, the rector began to pull aside the rubble to find the centuries-old cross which stood on the altar: he prayed silently that it had not been destroyed.

In Langenhoe itself, the devastation was equally complete. *The Essex Standard* of April 26th reported:

> The scene in this parish of two hundred and thirty souls is spoken of by eye-witnesses as most painful in the extreme – women and children rushed out of their houses in the greatest terror and alarm, many of them shrieking in the roads, while men were also startled and were unable for some time to understand or realise what had happened.
>
> How many of the poor people whose houses have thus been wrecked, are to find shelter for themselves and their families for some little time, is more than we can say. In scarcely any of the houses are the upper rooms tenantable, while owing to the chimneys which have fallen and interfered with the arrangements of the lower rooms, it is impossible to light fires.

The Lion public house was badly damaged, "the chimneys having fallen carrying with them part of the roof and the ceilings of the upper rooms", according to *The Standard*. "At the school much mischief was done, too, although fortunately the children had not assembled. The chimney seems to have fallen right through the roof of the school, and the building is split in every direction."

Several of the larger houses and mansions in the vicinity were hard hit: Langenhoe Hall was partly unroofed and Wick Farm and Crouch House "suffered very much". At Langenhoe Lodge, a Mr Pertwee reported that the "chimneys were thrown down, the walls much cracked, ceilings uplifted and bottles and chinaware thrown down and broken."

In the fields between Langenhoe and the larger neighbouring community of Fingringhoe, a group of farm workers were ploughing the land. According to a statement taken later by the Rector, Mr Parkinson, one of the men "saw the ground move some distance in front of him, then the horses stumbled and floundered about and the plough was thrown out of the furrow."

The man himself was thrown to the ground, and as he tried to rise, the whinnying of one of the plough horses brought his eyes in line with Langenhoe Church "which he saw thrown down". Another man in a field to the north of the Rectory was also toppled over and was terrified that "the ground was going to open up and swallow him".

In Fingringhoe "a large percentage" of the buildings belonging to the 650 residents were badly damaged, according to *The Essex Telegraph*. The Post Office lost its chimneys and the roof was swept almost entirely clean of tiles. The Postmaster, Mr Crickmar, who had just opened the shop for business, managed to dodge the falling debris and escaped into the street.

The nave roof and the walls of the parish church were extensively shattered, and The Hall, the property of Sir Robert Affleck, "lost the upper part of the western side of the front elevation" according to the subsequent builder's survey.

Another fine building, West House, had its entire tiles removed, two chimneys thrown down and the front so badly shaken it had to be speedily shored up to prevent it falling down. Mr J.S. Barnes' Ballast Quay farmhouse was similarly so extensively cracked as to require virtual rebuilding.

A bricklayer working on Mill House at Fingringhoe Haye had the narrowest escape from death in the vicinity. The man, named Potter, was on a ladder repairing the gable end of the house when the earthquake struck. *The Essex Telegraph* reported, "The shock so alarmed him that he jumped off, rolled across a roof, and as he was hastening away a brick or some hard material struck his head and he was thrown by the force of the blow into a ditch, where he lay until assistance came to him." The unfortunate Potter required urgent medical attention and was unable to work for some months afterward. (A photograph of The Mill House receiving attention from a group of builder's labourers shortly after the earthquake is reproduced in this book.)*

Just under two miles further along the road out of Fingringhoe and leading to Maldon was Abberton where, according to the local police constable, "hardly a house or cottage in the place has escaped damage. The wood built ones stood it best, but most of them are damaged." This small community of just over 200 people, sited at the crossing of the Maldon road by that of another running from Colchester to Mersea, lost virtually every chimney and few walls escaped being cracked and damaged.

Prior to the earthquake, several builders had been busy in the village, and their handiwork suffered heavily. A row of recently completed cottages near the public house were badly shaken and daylight could be seen through the cracks in several of them.

At the rectory, a building then nearing completion after nine months' work, every room was damaged, and the two huge chimney stacks, each weighing over three tons, were twisted and bent. After inspecting the damage, the builder, Mr F. Chancellor of Chelmsford, reported that although special care had been taken with the foundations, "still the building had received a most severe wrench which would put weeks of extra work on the job." The Rector, the Reverend J. Pilditch, found that his church had suffered almost as badly as his home, the structure being shaken, the windows smashed and most of the tiles wrenched from the roof.

An eyewitness was on hand to recount what happened at another new cottage just to the south of the village.

---

* *The Essex Herald* briefly reported another serious injury at Fringringhoe, though research has failed to identify the victim or what became of her. The item, published on April 28th, read: "A poor woman at Fingringhoe is seriously ill from being struck on the head by a chimney pot and knocked backwards over a pail, and she lies in a somewhat critical condition."

The shaking of the ground caused it to suffer severely, and about 20 feet of brickwork was thrown down from the gable along with the chimney. The occupant of this house, trying to dash outside at the moment of the disturbance, was driven back indoors by the falling debris and suffered bruises and cuts to his arms.

Three older cottages nearby lost all their tiles and the chimney stacks were thrown over into the gardens. One occupant working in the garden clung on to his spade for support but was thrown to the ground.

The chimney stack broke through the roof and into the main room of the small village school, spraying debris, timber and mortar across the empty desks and stools – the children had left only minutes before with their teacher for a short nature walk in the nearby fields.

The bakery belonging to Mr Felgate was also badly damaged, the oven and bake office shaft being demolished by the force of the blow. The same fate befell several nearby properties belonging to the local MP, Mr O.E. Coope.

Amongst all the destruction, however, two extraordinary phenomena were observed in Abberton. At Abberton House, the property of Mr John Bawtree, and occupied by his son Mr Edward Bawtree, all the huge chimneys had been partially turned round on their foundations without one being broken up: the fate of virtually every other stack in the vicinity. Mr Bawtree jnr later submitted a sketch of the strange damage to the investigators from the Essex Field Club – on whose activities we shall comment later – who remarked that it showed "the extremely complicated effects produced by the seismic movement".

It was in the village, too, that spring water added another dimension to the earthquake story, as *The Essex Telegraph* reported, "At Abberton we first heard of the phenomenon of spring water having been effected by the earthquake, a remarkable occurrence which was also noticed elsewhere. The spring close by was on Tuesday discoloured for some time and not fit for use." (In this context it is interesting to note that today much of the Abberton district is now under water, forming the bowl of a huge reservoir supplying water for Essex and Southern England.)

Journeying south-west, the Maldon road reaches Peldon,

another small rural community, which early reports believed to have been the most badly injured spot in the earthquake, and perhaps directly above its epicentre. In it lived 450 people.

Investigator, Raphael Meldola, writing in the cautious and restrained Essex Field Club report, said, "The damage here was considerable, the village having suffered more than any of the places mentioned, every house and cottage sustained more or less injury, some of the buildings having been rendered temporarily uninhabitable." *The Essex Chronicle* was more to the point: "The village presents a devastated and dilapidated condition."

The picturesque Peldon Rose Inn – still today one of the most attractive public houses in this corner of Essex – was typical of many other properties in the damage that it suffered. Standing invitingly just beside the causeway which leads to Mersea Island, the 400-year-old inn had its roof stripped of tiles, the walls cracked and bulged, and a large, sustantially built chimney stack broke through the centre of the roof, crashed through the floors and smashed into the

The *Peldon Rose* – a sketch from *The Illustrated London News* at the time of the earthquake

cellar below. A man walking past at the time said the whole building "appeared to heave upwards, and the middle of the roof to open, when the mass of falling bricks and chimney pots tumbled into the interior." According to late reports the landlord, Mr George Pullen, and his family "very narrowly escaped person injury" by dashing from the building when the debris began to fall. Experts who later examined the premises believed that it was only the iron stays fixed around the walls which had stopped the building from collapsing completely under the impact.

Just across the road from the inn stood Peldon Mill and here a second tragedy within the space of a few weeks was enacted for its owner, Mrs S. Went. *The Essex Telegraph* skilfully captured the heartbreak in its report:

Perhaps the saddest case of loss and discomfort – in the midst of thousands of sad illustrations of damage done by the shock – presented itself at the residence and business place of Mrs Went, a poor woman who had just lost her husband. He was a small miller, and had saved a little money and bought the mill, which she was now endeavouring to keep running.

The house was so far cracked and beaten about that access to the upper rooms could not be obtained by reason of the debris. The south wall bulged in a most threatening manner. The scene at the time of the shock must have been alarming, for furniture and glass were thrown about as if the building had had to resist a cannon ball.

The brick round house on which the mill stood had deep fissures in the walls, and the shaft of the engine-house had been cut in halves about midway up as if by a sword.

A miller's cottage adjoining was so much damaged that only the kitchen – and that not with safety – was available for shelter day and night, and this was all that nine persons had for household accommodation!

A later visitor to the shattered premises, Mr Wilson Marriage, described them as "choked up with debris" and "so badly cracked that they would have to be rebuilt entirely". Mr Wilson said that the inhabitants who were on the premises at the time of the earthquake told him they were thrown against the walls, and attempted to cling on to anything as furniture spun around them, glass and chinaware smashed and a large

A front page drawing from *The Illustrated Police News* of May 3rd 1884

The quay at Wivenhoe photographed from Lord Alfred Paget's yacht on the river Colne

Lord Alfred Paget's yacht, the *Santa Cecilia*, from which he and his crew watched the destruction of Wivenhoe

A row of ruined fishermen's cottages at Wivenhoe

A shattered quay-side house belonging to Mr George Harvey at Wivenhoe

The Anchor Inn at Wivenhoe where the landlord, Mr Dick Ham, and his wife had hairsbreadth escapes

Another group of damaged cottages in the cramped Sun Yard, Wivenhoe

The gas works at Wivenhoe—a scene of great drama during the earthquake

A roof open to the sky—the view which many householders in Wivenhoe and the surrounding district found after the earthquake

A view along the High Street, Colchester—Britain's oldest recorded town

The Lion Walk
Congregational
Church which lost its
steeple

Colchester Castle
which, despite its
size, was strongly
shaken by the tremor

The Bell Inn at Old Heath, Colchester, which a living eyewitness, Alfred Mason, saw being wrecked

One of the large fissures on Mersea Island. This picture was taken at St Peter's Well when the crack had virtually closed again

upright piano was moved from one side of a room to the other. *The Essex Standard* also managed to find its own exclusive little story of tragedy in the village.

A woman named King was engaged in setting plants in her garden when she was stunned by a falling brick, and as she was clinging to some pailings for support, she was struck on the back by some further considerable quantity of falling debris. It was at first thought that she was much injured, but she was soon seen by Mr Hugh Green, surgeon, and it was found that her case was not so serious as was supposed. Her home, however, was most seriously shaken and dilapidated.

A third news story – also exclusive to the paper which printed it, *The Essex Weekly News* – added yet another personal drama to the event: "The cottage of the local policeman, PC Nicholls has been much knocked about, and he himself had a narrow escape from death. He was stooping for some wood just outside his back door when the crash came, and the materials of the chimney fell within a few inches of his head."

But while people fortuitously escaped serious injury,* the same was not true of buildings, although few suffered as extensively as Peldon's picturesque and ancient parish church. This stone edifice which had towered over the small community for almost six hundred years "was found much damaged" according to *The Essex Telegraph*.

On the square Norman tower was one of the old beacons used in days long ago, and a portion of this, together with some of the tower itself, were hurled on the roof of the nave through which the masonry crashed into the Church below. Huge pieces of stone and brickwork also fell in all directions into the Churchyard,

---

* I learned of one further narrow escape as I was completing this book from an actual eyewitness, ninety-one-year-old Mr Charles Nice, who was just a year old at the time. He was living in the White House, Peldon, and was sitting in a high chair in front of the fire when the earthquake occurred. Bricks fell down the chimney and covered him with soot from head to foot. It also caused the front door lintel of the house to go lopsided and this remained untouched until 1941/2 when the owners at that time decided to straight it as they felt it might detract from the selling value of the house. But, according to Mr Crisp's daughter, Mrs M. Carter, "when my father told them the earthquake had caused it, they were very sorry they had not left it as it was!"

while a wide fissure up the side of the tower seems to point to the
fact that for safety sake it will have to be pulled down. The walls
also were greatly out of level and bulging.

The rectory, nearby, was similarly battered, the chimney
stacks falling through the roof and narrowly missing the
Rector of Peldon, the Reverend Carter Hall, who was at work
in his study. As a result, all the upstairs rooms in the house
became uninhabitable.

For the rector, the destruction of the nave roof of the church
proved an added blow, for it had only recently been re-roofed
after the money to pay for this work had been painstakingly
raised over the previous five years. As he surveyed the
ruination of his beloved church, the Reverend Hall must
surely have thought ruefully to himself of the warnings which,
along with several others, he had voiced in previous weeks
about 'something being in the air'. Both he and his daughter
had heard a 'subterranean rumbling' about two months
previously and were convinced it portended danger of some
kind. His forebodings now lay in grim actuality everywhere he
looked in his parish.

Two days after the earthquake, when the whole district had
been surveyed, there seemed little doubt that the most
extensively damaged property was Strood Villa, standing
beside the causeway leading from Peldon to Mersea, and
belonging to the wealthy and highly-esteemed local surgeon,
Mr Hugh Green. Built in 1860 of substantial stone and
brickwork, the building was so devastated that "it is a marvel
that it stands at all", to quote *Symons's Monthly Meteorological
Magazine*. One of the local newspapers, *The Essex Standard*,
provides the grim details of the tragedy which occurred here:

Mr Green's house is literally split from end to end – there is not a
sound wall either inside or outside standing; all the windows in
the house are smashed, the cap stone to the porch at the entrance
is down, as also are the chimneys, one stack of which falling upon
Mr Green's consulting room, completely demolished the latter.

Mr Green, who had fortunately left the consulting room only a
few minutes before, was in the surgery adjoining at the time, and
here he was startled by the bottles from the shelves falling upon
and around him, perfectly smothering him with their contents. A
massive pierglass over the mantlepiece in the drawing room was

wrenched from the wall, and fell into the middle of the room, lustres and other ornaments were strewn about, and the general furniture of the room disarranged.

The upstairs rooms suffered as much or more than the downstairs ones, and are now altogether uninhabitable – in fact, almost the only room in the house that could be used is the kitchen. Fortunately none of the occupants sustained injury, and Mr Green said that he considered he owed his own safety solely to the fact that his wife had temporarily displaced him from the consulting room in order to have it cleaned; he had not left it ten seconds before the crash came.

The Essex Field Club investigators made a particular study of the Villa and reported that it "certainly presented one of the worst cases of destruction that came under our notice". They added in conclusion, "the suddenness of the shock was well exemplified by the fact that a bird (probably a starling) had been caught in a crack under the eaves of the roof and there died, the remains being still visible on the occasion of a visit of the Club to the district on August 4th 1884."

The unforuntate Mr Green was a close friend of the Reverend Musselwhite, the Vicar of Mersea, who lived just across the causeway. He had been another of the local people who had felt the subterranean rumblings in the district before the actual earthquake and was convinced that they forecast danger of some kind. He had discussed the matter with the Reverend Musselwhite, and may even have been instrumental in making the vicar pick up his pen and write a letter about the matter to *The Essex Standard* on April 24th.

"My object in troubling you with this letter," Reverend Musselwhite wrote to the editor, "is to mention what I have not yet noticed in the papers – that we had a kind of premonition of this calamity some time before it happened.

"On the early morning of Monday, February 18th, at about 1.20 a.m. we had a sharp shock, which was momentary, and seemed to lift the bedstead on which I was lying. This shock was felt by several in the house, and by people in different parts of the island. The officers of the Coastguard got up and dressed, and walked along the shore. Our surgeon, Mr Hugh Green, whose house sustained much injury, felt this former shock most distinctly, and spoke of it to me the same day."

The vicar concluded simply, "I thought it well that this fact should be known, as it is plain both shocks were due to a like cause, and felt most distinctly at the same places."

What the Reverend Musselwhite could not know at that time was that his sentiments were shared by quite a few other people: people who had the uneasy feeling that warnings had been overlooked if not actually ignored. His letter, in fact, was to be the first of several instances of premonition and even precognition about the earthquake which, although recorded at the time, were in such diverse places that they have not been brought together as a whole for examination until now. We shall be studying this strange aspect of our story and some of the bizarre forms it took in a later chapter.

The earthquake, however, had not confined its destruction to this small corner of Essex alone. The "wave of terror", as one eyewitness had called it, had struck widely and much further afield ... indeed, to the very heart of the British Empire, its far-famed capital city, London.

6 Terror across England

The Houses of Parliament wore their time-honoured aspect of dignity and authority in the warm morning sunlight. Around Parliament Square hansom cabs were clip-clopping businessmen to their offices, while a multitude of pedestrians – clerks, girl shop assistants, messenger boys and a variety of other London workers – hurried about their tasks. The city was alive with the sounds of the fast developing day, and from the river Thames the booming of the occasional horn blended with the cranking and groaning of dockside machinery.

The House had not yet begun sitting for the day, and MPs in their top hats and frock coats were arriving singly or in small groups at the main entrance. The two police constables on duty at the gate were conscious of a more than usually solemn air about most of the members. Their salutes of recognition were in the main greeted with the merest formal acknowledgement as the men hurried by and into the parliament building.

Certainly there was much on their minds: public concern was growing daily about the plight of General Gordon and his soldiers beleagured in the Sudan, and those who belonged to the ruling party, the Liberals, were facing a division on an important bill which might well end in defeat for the government. It promised to be a day of sharp exchanges on both issues, with the Prime Minister, Mr Gladstone, in line for some hostility from his opponents.

In the Lobbies, several groups of Whig and Tory MPs were already huddled together discussing tactics over the Gordon affair. General Gordon, a hero of the Crimean and Chinese wars, and for some years past an ambassador in far flung corners of the British Empire, was a particular favourite of the British people. When, early in 1884, English garrisons in the Sudan had been beseiged by native rebels led in an insurrection by the Mahdi, he had been a popular choice to effect the rescue of these troops. However, since his arrival in the Sudan, things had gone disastrously wrong, and by late April he himself was firmly surrounded by the Mahdi's army at Khartoum. Although news of the general reaching England was scant, concern grew daily, and *The Times'* leading article for the morning of April 22nd 1884 demanded action from Parliament to allay "the feeling of anxiety about this matter which prevails in the country". These sentiments were shared by not a few of the MPs gathered in the Lobbies that morning.

Mr Gladstone himself had already expressed the belief – which he was to reiterate again – that "Khartoum is not in imminent and immediate danger", and he clung steadfastly to this view in the face of attacks from all sides, including one strongly-worded challenge from the formidable Lord Randolph Churchill. (It was, of course, his failure in this episode – Khartoum was not relieved until the following year, by which time Gordon was dead – that seriously damaged his prestige, and led with other foreign issues to the eventual downfall of his government in 1885.)

Another blow that was to fall on Gladstone that April day was the defeat by 185 votes to 161 of an amendment to the Contagious Diseases (Animals) Bill. It was, in the words of *The Times*, "the sharpest check the Government has received in the present Parliament".

Important, and far-reaching, though both these events were, another drama was to upset the calm of the Houses of Parliament that morning. A drama that some people saw as a sign of the gradual undermining which was taking place in the British way of life.

At "about 9.19 a.m." as assembly was already under way, there were "violent tremors and a rumbling noise" throughout the entire buildings. Members were stopped in their tracks, jolted against the walls, or felt papers and briefcases jerked from their hands. "It seemed as if all the rooms of the building, not to mention the city as a whole, were violently shaken," *The Daily Mail* reported, "fittings and gas lights were displaced and those inside sickened to their stomachs." An MP standing on the balcony looking at the Thames at the moment of the shock, staggered against the balustrade and saw "a wave about three foot high sweep across the river and swamp several small boats at St. Paul's Pier."

There was a bigger shock in store for workmen engaged on repairs on the Victoria Tower, at the extreme end of the House of Lords. *The Police News* gives us the most dramatic record:

> In one of the four pinnacles of the tower six workmen were employed. They were busily engaged at their work some little distance apart, when they were all greatly alarmed at the sudden undulatory motion. They collected together in amazement, and *another shock coming on*, they instantly withdrew from the pinnacle to the roof of the tower, near the flag staff.
>
> Here they felt the tower still vibrate, and they immediately fled to the ground, where they reported the matter, attributing the shaking of the tower to the wind. They were informed that no wind that ever blew would have the smallest effect upon such a massive structure.

This account is interesting because of its mention of a second shock, an occurrence recorded in one or two other instances. However, whether there was one or more disturbances at the House, it is now impossible to substantiate, and due to the lack of corroborative evidence, it seems likely that it was the vibration of the tower, which began after the passing of the shock, which confused the workmen into thinking that there had been a second occurrence. This was most probably not the case closer to the epicentre, as we shall discuss later.

The upheaval was also noticed strongly in the House of Commons Library, where people and furniture swayed, and books were scattered on the floor.

First reactions to the shock suggested an explosion, possibly in the cellars of the parliament buildings, and officials were despatched immediately to investigate. According to one or two newspapers there were light-hearted comments made by several opposition MPs to the effect that 'Guy Fawkes' Gladstone was responsible, and had caused the disturbance to distract attention from his political plight!

More seriously, there were fears that there had been a large explosion somewhere in the vicinity of London caused by the notorious Dynamiters who were then active in England. There had been several such cases in the newspapers in recent months, and even the previous day at the Police Court in Birmingham a certain James Francis Egan had appeared and been remanded, charged with "conspiring with John Daly, alias Denman, to cause an explosion in the United Kingdom, likely to endanger life and property". *The Times* had already summarised the situation, "Notwithstanding the vigilance exercised by the English detectives … the members of the dynamite organisation hold secret meetings and are evidently in league with such Communists as *Citi en Allemane* and with the Nihilist chiefs."

How widespread this fear became can be judged by the fact that *The Essex Standard* noted, "Another reason assigned for the phenomenon was that the Government Stores at Woolwich or Purfleet had been destroyed by the agency of some of the diabolical schemes of the Dynamiters." Similarly, *The East Essex and Halstead Times* reported, "Many people concluded that a dreadful explosion had occurred, while to the minds of not a few came the memory of recent actions of the much-loathed 'Dynamite Crew'."

But in such a cosmopolitan city as London, with its many widely-travelled citizens, the majority of people realized what had happened almost immediately – not that it made their surprise any the less. As *The Times* reported, "No earthquake has been experienced in and around the metropolis to such a widespread extent for a great many years."

The shock was most severely felt in the upper stories of buildings and large numbers of people were made to feel sick by the trembling of the ground. The Strand and Charing Cross area were most noticeably affected, goods were thrown over in shops, lamps and bells were jangled and some broken, and people shaken where they sat or stood.

At the offices of *The Lancet*, compositors felt the movement "with such distinctness that they all left their work and hurried into the street, under the impression that the building was about to fall." A report from the magazine stated that one workman said the case he was working at began to rock so violently that he suspected a practical joke: when he realized no one was close enough to have touched it "he at once came to the conclusion that something out of the common had occurred." The statement added, "A proof reader attached to the paper says that the ceiling appeared about to fall, and that he felt the floor oscillating under him. The men were so panic-stricken that they refused to resume work until a surveyor had been sent for to certify to the safe condition of the building."

In the Hyde Park area many doors were bent in their frames and would not close properly; clocks were also stopped. In the fashionable shopping centre of Regent Street much the same thing happened and many shop doors were flung open and goods tumbled from counters and shelves. In Oxford Street, the shaking and rumbling caused a number of people on the pavement to be overcome by nausea, and four clerks working on the second floor of Messrs H and M Southwell were so frightened by the noise and movement that they fled into the street.

There was one near tragedy at the Old Bailey where a gas lamp was broken open by the upheaval and this soon set furniture and fittings alight. It was at first feared that the whole of the famous old edifice of law and justice might be gutted, but swift action by members of the staff and the speedy arrival of the fire brigade averted a disaster.

London's railway stations also felt the earthquake, and buildings, trains and passengers were rocked by the passing 'wave'. Tall factories throughout the city moved from side to side, like that of Messrs Hazel, Watson and Viney in Hatton Garden, a five-storey building, which vibrated so strongly that "a large number of men began to rush away in alarm."

Hospitals, too, were disturbed, and there was an amusing incident reported at St Bartholomew's where a medical student heard the rumbling sound and then saw some teeth suspended in a glass jar opening and closing as if in speech. A skeleton in the same room also shook and trembled as if "performing some mad dance".

Medical men provided two of the most interesting personal accounts of the earthquake in London. The first, Surgeon-Major W.C.B. Eatwell of Kensington Gardens, writing in *Nature* magazine of May 1st 1884, said, "The sensation was that of being born rather on water than solid earth, and as I had already had experience of an earthquake shock in India, I suspected that this disturbance was of the same nature. It is perhaps interesting to note that among its many effects, it caused my usually reliable watch to run on a pace, so that by the end of the day it was fifteen minutes fast."

The following day a letter appeared in *The Kilburn Times* from Dr Henry T. Wharton of St George's Road, Kilburn:

> The earthquake which occurred on Tuesday morning was more widely felt in Kilburn than your brief note would imply. Many of my patients noticed it, although none of them thought of assigning the right cause to the phenomenon.
>
> A lady in St George's Road fancied that a traction engine must have been passing, only she wondered why she could hear no noise; she was always curious to feel an earthquake, but she has no desire to repeat this, her first experience of one. More than one member of a family in Priory Road wondered why the furniture, and especially the ornaments on the mantlepiece, rocked so strangely, and they observed to one another, 'If we had still been in Lisbon, we should have thought it was an earthquake.'* And an old nurse in Sutherland Gardens was so terrified that she dared not get out of bed until the lady's maid came and assured her that the end of the world had not come.

The family of Mr Gunn, a theatrical manager, living in Russell Square, have also provided a personal impression of the disturbance. Mr Gunn himself was asleep in bed at the time, when he was awakened by the motion of the bedstead. "He at once ascribed it to a shock of earthquake," said *The Daily Telegraph*. "His wife, who had experienced similar sensations in America, states that the motion was of a gentle nature, like the slow rocking of a cradle. Her niece, however, sleeping in the adjoining compartment, states that she felt a more violent motion, it appearing that the bedroom floor was moving up and down."

The same newspaper also informed its readers,

> The shock was slightly felt by many inhabitants of Pimlico and Chelsea. It is affirmed by a number of persons residing in the vicinity of Chelsea Barracks that at about a quarter past nine a kind of rumbling noise was distinctly heard. Some of the persons residing in the streets immediately at the back of the Barracks believed that it was the beating of drums in the barrack-yard preparatory to a march-out, while others imagined that either an explosion had taken place in the locality, or that a large quantity

---

* It is recorded that the famous Lisbon earthquake of 1755 "troubled the waters of the fish pond, called Peerless Pool, in the London City Road", according to *Nature* magazine. (*The Kilburn Times*)

of timber was being removed at the timber yard adjoining the workshop of the Board of Works at Ebury-Bridge.

The shock was also registered at Woolwich, where it caused considerable concern at the Royal Arsenal. Mr Wallace, the manager of the government establishment, said that he felt the trembling of the ground quite distinctly, and items were thrown to the floor and several people shaken from their chairs. Sample bottles and other articles on the desks and shelves were also visibly shaken. A special correspondent of *The Times* reporting from the site added, "Some persons attributed the occurrence to the bursting of a heavy gun at the proof butts in the Government marshes, adjoining the Royal Arsenal."

Perhaps the most typical experience of all Londoners was that reported by Mr Alfred Crookes of Holland Park Terrace, who said, "As my wife and I were sitting reading after breakfast, I felt a sort of sidelong heaving of the chair and a sinking, giddy sensation in my head, and at the same moment the folding doors, which were shut, bumped backwards and forwards, and the windows back and front of the house rattled sharply." With the imperturbability of his social position, Mr Crookes added, "I looked at the clock immediately, and remarked to my wife that it must have been an earthquake."

Unshaken as Mr Crookes appeared to be, the effect of the disturbance on much of London had been frightening and became an immediate topic of widespread gossip. Yet, as the day passed, it became obvious that the city had escaped lightly and the emphasis of news coverage was directed to more traditional items – perhaps less undermining of the very basis of British life – such as Mr Gladstone and his problems in the Sudan and with Animal Diseases.

By the following morning the earthquake, at least as far as most of the national press was concerned, was being considered as a secondary matter, confined to the inside pages of the newspapers, with the amount and extent of damage considerably minimised.

Not so in Essex, though, where the bruised and shaken population confronted with devastation and ruin on all sides, were already calling it with considerable feeling and justification. "The Great English Earthquake".

Ruined cottages at Abberton – from *The Illustrated London News*

From its epicentre, now generally agreed to be in the vicinity of the Essex villages of Wivenhoe, Peldon and Abberton, the earthquake rumbled and trembled across an area of 53,000 square miles of English countryside. Although it would be impossible to draw an exact circumference, the outward radius was approximately 150 miles from the centre, though disturbances were registered far beyond this limit.

The most exact data published at the time, by The Essex Field Club, gives the following distances as the furthest points reached by the earthquake. (The Club took as its centre point the village of Abberton):

East: Ostend. Longitude 2 58′ E.
West: Street in Somersetshire. Longitude 2 45′W.
South: Freshwater, Isle of Wight. Latitude 20 40′N.
North: Brigg in Lincolnshire. Latitude 53 33′N.
The furthest points measured from the centre were:
North-North West: Brigg, 135 miles.
North-West: Altrincham, 180 miles.
West-South West: Street, 170 miles.
South-West: Freshwater, 135 miles.
South-South East   Boulogne, 90 miles.
South-East: Ostend, 100 miles.

Although much useful material was collected at the time of the earthquake, a great deal more was certainly contributed to scattered sources, now destroyed or no longer obtainable, and therefore a complete and exhaustive coverage of the event is impossible to compile. Indeed, even if all this data was available, such would be the size that a simple listing of each point of incident would almost certainly demand a book on its own. Hence, in this section, I have confined myself to noting only the more important places where upheaval was recorded, and in particular those which help to underline the extent and strength of the earthquake.

This particular aspect of the story has proved one of the most fascinating for me. While much of the Essex material has been centrally located, reports from other districts have been scattered through a variety of publications and sources – not to mention localities – and drawing them painstakingly together has been rather like working on a jigsaw puzzle when you can never be quite sure if some pieces are not already irretrievably lost. I would not now claim to have completed the picture entirely, but enough is in place to give the reader a chance to judge the enormity of what happened. Comparing the reports against a map of England will heighten this impression still further.

To the north, as we have seen, the disturbance was recorded 180 miles away from its source at Altrincham in Cheshire. A tremor was "distinctly felt" by a Mr A. Wimpory, who confirmed his suspicion that there had been an upheaval with several neighbours in the town. Although his initial claim that the country must have been hit by a substantial earthquake, probably in the far south, was greeted with some scepticism, he was fully vindicated by newspaper reports on the following days.

In the West, reports were forthcoming from both Devon and Somerset, provided by men of unimpeachable authority, Mr J. Edmund Clark, of Street, a geographer and correspondent of *Nature* magazine, believed he felt a tremor in the town, but was not prepared to confirm this until he interviewed an invalid lady living nearby who said she felt her bed move "strongly" at 9.20 a.m. Writing in *Nature* on May 1st, 1884, he said, "Probably one of the extreme limits of the action of the earthquake was at Street, ten miles beyond the Mendip main anticline. There it was felt by an invalid lady who mentioned it at midday dinner, only a few hours after, no news having been received, of course, from other parts."

At Exeter in Devon, a lady lying on a couch felt a "slight movement of the earth" and her experience was subsequently duplicated by others, including a Dr H. Kingdom, in a report in the *Transactions of the Devon Association.*

Far to the south of England, in Hampshire, the details committed to paper proved the most fullsome of any for the fringes of the disturbance. At Farnborough Station, a Mrs Edmund Wodehouse of Minley Grange, reported that "between 9.16 and 9.22 a.m. I was in bed and distinctly felt a vibration, followed by a rocking of the bed from side to side." Mrs Wodehouse estimated the duration of the shock at about 30 seconds, and there appeared to be "seven distinct heaves". Crockery in the house rattled, tea was spilled from a cup and the shock was also felt by two servants in the house.

At Portsmouth, the shock was widely felt and there were numerous reports of light furniture being shaken. Across the Solent, on the Isle of Wight, the Hon. Hallam Tennyson, who was in bed in his home, 'Farringford' in Freshwater, felt "the bed gently oscillate and saw the bed hangings swing for about 15 seconds." The clock in the drawing room was stopped by the tremor. A Mr J.W. Woodruff at East Cowes reported feeling two distinct vibrations which lasted several seconds, and added that he heard similar reports from Ryde.

Two reports which also came to hand showed that the earthquake had made its presence felt across the English Channel, although it was not until the following day that the cause was ascertained. *Symons's Monthly Meteorological Magazine* reported, "Shock felt in several parts of Boulogne at 9.30 a.m. Paris times (= 9 hours 20 minutes 39 seconds, Greenwich time)".

From Belgium, Mr Oliver Lodge, a barrister-at-law, of 14, Rue Louise, Ostend, noted: "Shock felt between 9 and 9.30; bed oscillated two or three times from north-west to south-east; room shaken, duration about two seconds."

Within the confines of these furthermost points, however,

the action has been much more dramatic as a county-by-county survey discloses.

Kent, on the heel of England, and facing Essex across the Thames Estuary, naturally received a considerable buffeting, particularly along the north coastline between Rochester and Margate. *The Times* reported on April 23rd: "Great alarm was felt at the Sheerness dockyard, and telegrams were despatched to various places in the neighbourhood to ascertain whether an explosion had occurred. The utmost uncertainty prevailed as to the cause until the arrival of the evening papers. At Rochester, Strood and Sheerness the shock was violent."

Throughout the county houses shook, doors and windows trembled, bells rang, furniture and crockery were moved and occasionally broken, and a noise "like distant thunder" rumbled below ground. The strongest impacts were noted at Beckenham, Canterbury, Herne Bay, Maidstone, Westgate-on-Sea, Whitstable and Dover. At Chiselhurst a number of people were rolled out of their beds, and one lady whose bed was "violently shaken" thought there must have been an explosion nearby. At Strood the Board School was "so shaken that the masters immediately dismissed the scholars".

A lady lying in bed in Tonbridge felt a push of the bed so strongly that she asked her little girl, who was in the room at the time, why she was shaking it. The child denied having anything to do with the movement, it being made of iron in any case, and much too heavy for her to have moved. In this particular district there were said to be "consecutive tremulous rockings, such as would be produced by a heavy traction engine".

In the adjacent county of Surrey, the tremor was similarly felt, and carefully noted at Kew Observatory by Mr G.M. Whipple, FRAS, who wrote, "We have a good record of the earthquake in our magnetograph traces. It took place at 9.18 a.m. G.M.T., deflecting the bifilar magnet, which moves north and south considerably, and the declination magnet, which swings east and west slightly."

People in bed were particularly affected by the shock, and a great many clocks were stopped. A Mrs K.M. Bernard of Reigate reported, "I was sitting up in bed in an upstairs room when I distinctly felt the bed shake from head to foot two or three times, and after a pause, shake again in the same way. I remarked on it to a servant who came up after a short time, and said that I feared there had been a dynamite explosion in London.''

Other similar reports came in from Battersea, Brixton, Croydon, Dorking, Esher, Richmond and Wimbledon where tennis players engaged in a match had the sudden bizarre experience of the ground beneath their feet moving and the tennis ball bouncing madly out of line!

The "rumbling sound" which moved across Sussex was reported by Mr C.L. Prince from the Observatory at Crowborough, and confirmed by householders in several centres including Brighton, Eastbourne, Hastings and St Leonards. Mrs E. Rider Cook who was in bed at St Leonard's said she "suddenly felt the bed sway and rock to and fro". In Eastbourne a number of houses suffered cracked ceilings and along the seafront a number of windows broke.

The sound heard in neighbouring Berkshire differed somewhat and was described by several people in Reading "as if the wind was rising". The shock was most clearly recorded at Marlow, Hurley, Pinkney's Green and Sulhampstead; again the strongest feelings being registered by people on the second or higher floors of buildings.

At Bristol and Cheltenham in Gloucestershire there was considerable anxiety after the shock – which was preceded by a rumbling sound and most strongly felt along the river Avon. The lower parts of Bristol were shaken, and several instances of damage to property were reported. At Cheltenham a Mr C. Pooley of Northumberland Lodge claimed there were two shocks, separated by a second or two, but he said he heard no noise at all. In *Nature* magazine it was noted that walls were seen to move at Stroud; crockery was broken and one man in bed was actually turned over by the oscillations.

Forty miles away, Oxford University felt the impact of the tremor, and several of the colleges had their work disrupted by books and stationery being tumbled on to the floor. Elsewhere in Oxfordshire, a sensation of shaking was recorded at Bicester, Banbury and Watlington. At Shirburn Castle, near Watlington, the Countess of Macclesfield recorded her experience, "I was sitting at my dressing table at 9.20 when I felt an oscillation of the floor which lasted about three seconds and seemed to be from north to south. Two ladies in the upper floor of the Castle felt it also." This account is particularly interesting as, in 1755, the great Lisbon earthquake registered on the moat that surrounds the castle by simultaneously agitating the water on two different sides.

On the river Thames at Marlow in Buckinghamshire, many of the small boats which had taken to the water for a quiet day's cruising were rocked backwards and forwards by the 'wave' of the earthquake. Boats in the vicinity of Temple Lock were particularly badly buffeted, and more than one crew were convinced they had "run foul of something". Other places in the county where the shock was reported, according to Mr Alfred H. Cocks, MA, included Banbury, Abingdon, Taplow and Princes Risborough.

To the north-west, Worcestershire experienced only a gentle trembling, although in the city of Worcester people in a row of houses at Severn Terrace ran into the street when their walls began to shake and small items of furniture and decoration fell to the floor. At the porcelain works in the town, the upheaval spilled liquids and overturned containers.

Moving north into the very heart of England, Warwickshire experienced stronger oscillations than several of its neighbours. Birmingham, particularly, was extensively shaken, and two of the largest restaurants in the city, the *Central* and the *Court*, reported a large amount of crockery and glassware shaken from the shelves and broken. Houses and offices similarly suffered with loose items toppled over on to the floor and there were reports of actual cracks in walls and ceilings in the Edgbaston and Hay Mills districts. In Leamington a number of people complained that the disturbance "produced a feeling of nausea" and some of these spoke of there having been two shocks "with a marked pause between them", according to a Mrs M. Saunders. In some districts there was very little movement of the ground, although "a low rumbling like a gust of wind" was heard.

Further north, in Shropshire, Staffordshire, Derbyshire and Nottingham, the trembling was fairly gentle, although in places such as Sidbury and Brignorth (Shropshire),

Wolverhampton (Staffs), Derby and Nottingham furniture was overturned, doors flung open, windows rattled and crockery knocked about or broken.

Lincolnshire, on the east coast, again took something of a buffeting, and there was damage reported at Boston (where Mr William Bedford "felt the tremor most distinctly" at his steam mill), Brigg, Crowland, Skegness, Spilsby, Stamford, Sutton Bridge ("rooms were shaken and windows rattled", according to Mr H.G. Grimley) and at Partney where "the ground vibrated violently as thought a train were rushing past." There was a drama at Long Sutton where workmen repairing a church steeple felt it oscillate sharply and had to cling to their scaffolding in terror. "The men were convinced it was going to fall and hurried down", according to a local report. "One man was actually thrown to the ground by the movement and suffered head injuries which required medical attention."

Workmen were also subjected to moments of fright in Leicestershire, particularly in the city of Leicester and Market Harborough. In Leicester the shock "was distinctly felt in many parts of the town, especially in Stonygate, the highest part, where furniture and ornaments were moved, and houses were felt to oscillate." In a room sixty feet above the ground in Messrs R. Walker & Son's factory, the whole construction swayed, machinery 'clanked' ominously and for several moments the workers clung panic-stricken to the walls. Another report from Market Harborough by a Mr C.A. Markham says that "at Messrs Symington's factory the building rocked so much that people at work in the lantern room thought it was about to fall."

The same county also produced an interesting letter which must have been common to many thousands of people in districts on the further reaches of the earthquake's impact. The writer is a Mr W. Clement Ley of Ashby Parva:

I was in bed writing at the time, which was about 9.19 a.m. G.M.T. by my watch, when I heard a roaring noise in the east, which made me look to a window facing east by south. Almost simultaneously, I heard a fall of soot and some pieces of mortar, and then I became conscious that my bed was swaying. The shock I computed to last five seconds, and the oscillations – to which I paid careful attention, having had experience of earthquakes long ago – seemed about two per second. I lay perfectly still, instead of looking at the watch. Two servants, occupied in separate rooms on the same floor as I was on myself, heard the noise, and complained that they were seized with giddiness. The shock seemed to me to be marked by far less noise – I mean subterranean noise – but by what one could call 'more swing and far less tremor', than that of October 1863, which I felt at Sellack, in Herefordshire, where some houses were injured on that occasion.

Hardly a town or village in Northamptonshire escaped being shaken by the earthquake, and damage was caused in several places including Northampton where an old Roman wall about two feet thick was knocked down. A distinct "swaying movement" of houses was felt here according to Mr C.A. Markham who said the accompanying noise was "like the rumbling of a wagon". Throughout the county furniture was moved, crockery vibrated and broken, and numerous people made to feel ill. Principle reports came from Ecton, Eye, Guildsborough, Kettering, Nassington, Peterborough, Sywell and Weedon. At Wellingborough, said Mr Markham, "The shock was felt in many parts of the town, notably in the warehouses of Messrs. Watkin and Messrs. Brown. At the Club, the ceiling cracked and fell, and clocks stopped."

Getting closer to the epicentre of the earthquake, in Hertforshire and Middlesex, one finds an almost endless list of similar experiences, with homes shaken and occasionally cracked and damaged, people briefly overcome by nausea, and a wild cacophony of bells ringing, crockery jangling and glassware smashing. Other towns in Middlesex suffered much as London had done, with Harrow, Isleworth, Northolt and Pinner registering the upheaval "strongly" and Enfield reporting a "rocking sensation" which caused cracks in a considerable number of houses and walls.

In Hertfordshire, the Reverend Frederick Ragg of Masworth Rectory, Tring, had a somewhat unusual viewpoint on the disturbances as he revealed in a letter to *Nature* magazine on May 8th:

I was on the scaffolding erected for repairs to the church. At a little past nine, I felt the church give what seemed like a fierce shudder. By shudder, I mean that a sort of vibration began, which almost instantly increased in intensity, reached a climax, and then rapidly decreased and died away.

A moment after a whirlwind followed ... which caused pictures to move, flower pots to rock and windows to shake. No noise was heard except the clatter caused by the rattling of the buildings.

Bishops Stortford felt the tremor "distinctly" and at Messrs Slater and Sons's tailoring establishment the employees rushed downstairs thinking the workroom at the top of the old fashioned house was falling outwards. Alarm was also caused at the London and County Bank, the steam mill in South Street and at the workhouse. There was trouble, too, at St Albans where the gas works were shaken "violently", and at the offices of *The Hertfordshire Mercury* terrified employees attributed the upheaval to a "terrible explosion" at the gunpowder works in Waltham Abbey not far away.

Cambridge University, like Oxford, felt the earthquake distinctly, and in the colleges a rumbling sound was heard, walls heaved and doors were thrown open. Some old pieces of masonry were also dislodged and one pedestrian was hurt by a falling chimney. Mr J.H. Turner, the postmaster, was lying ill in bed at the time and was rolled "first one way and then back again several times". Mr Albert Waters of Mill Road recorded what was the general experience in a letter to the local paper:

> The earthquake was felt here very plainly. I was looking around my marine aquaria when the wave passed under Cambridge. My attention was particularly on the aquarium in which I keep shrimp, mussels and sand-loving annelids, and this was tilted up so much that the sand at the shallow end was quite uncovered by the water.
>
> I remember, too, that I was sensible of a slight giddiness at the time and the house and everything in it seemed to be moving. I had no suspicion of the real cause, but thought for a moment it was a slight faintness, as I had not then breakfasted.

Elsewhere in Cambridgeshire, the disturbance unnerved the populace, giving a particular fright to the Reverend F.W. Joy, the Minor Canon of Ely, who felt the cathedral move, heard tiles rattle on the roof and saw the church bell ropes swinging from side to side. The instruments at the Cambridge

Observatory, which were at the time undergoing slight repairs, were so disturbed that it was some minutes before work could recommence. Sadly, because of these repairs, certain observations which the instruments could have made of the earthquake, were lost.

The sound noticed in Norfolk was "of a heavy traction engine passing" and the strong upheaval caused panic and some damage to property in Diss, Harleston, Lynn, Norwich, Thetford and Yarmouth. At Ditchingham, near Bungay, the silk crepe factory was shaken and the machinery began to "grind" during what appeared to the workers to be three oscillations.

The best personal report from the county was made by a Dr Donald Day at the Norfolk and Norwich Hospital in Norwich who wrote the following day, "I was reclining in an easy chair when I heard a rumbling as if some very heavy engine might be passing. At the same time the whole hospital oscillated, and of course my chair, too, in a direction north and south. The oscillations appeared to me to come from the south; they were five or six apparently and did not last more than ten seconds."

Suffolk, as the county immediately adjoining Essex to the north, received the first brunt of the shock after it had passed across the primary district. *The Suffolk Times & Mercury* reported dramatically,

A very distinct shock was felt throughout the district about 9.18 a.m. on Tuesday morning. Considerable alarm was created, and the wildest possible rumours were speedily afloat.

Comparatively few people were, however, bold enough to express an opinion that the shock was produced by an earthquake. Amongst the reports current was one which was stoutly insisted upon by a constable from an outlying parish, that the House of Commons had been blown up by the Fenians. Another rumour was to the effect that a terrible explosion had occurred at Colchester.

The news that a severe shock of earthquake had been experienced in the neighbourhood of Colchester rapidly ran through the area, and for a time great excitement and consternation prevailed.

In Ipswich, one of the most important towns in the region

and comparable in size to Colchester, the citizens had experienced similar terror to those in the ancient Essex city. Buildings had been severely shaken – particularly in the western part of the city "where they rocked like boats" said one eyewitness – tiles and chimney stacks had rained down on early morning pedestrians, and factories and offices were abandoned by frightened workers. Windows and doors cracked and broke, several water mains burst and bells throughout the town rang wildly. "Many of the inhabitants," wrote the *East Anglian Daily Times*, "were so much alarmed that they ran out of their houses, and several women fainted from the shock."

One lady who managed to keep her composure and provide an unusual angle on the disturbance was Mrs Ellen Biddell of Henley Road, Ipswich. She reported,

> I was lying in bed with my face towards a large window, watching the clouds in the north-east part of the sky, when all at once the clouds appeared to go and pass in every direction, and mix up together in a remarkable manner. Then came an awful rumbling sound under the bed, which heaved up.
>
> I started upright, and saw the north wall of the room bend in and outward, and the pictures on the wall flap. I saw the trees in rows from east to west shaking, not as if by wind, but as by a hand quickly shaking their stems.

At Ipswich Railway Station, the station-master, Mr Nibloe, felt a "strong vibration" and then a jarring noise. His first thought was that a train must have run off the line, the noise being "so similar to that of the wheels of an engine grinding along the line".

In the Customs House the shock was felt "to an alarming extent" according to *The Essex Telegraph*. "The whole building vibrated, and in one office a large press standing about eight feet high, swayed backwards and forwards, so much so that some of the officials rushed out of the building."

Several dozen people suffered slight injuries from falling masonry, while a boy getting coal in Princes Street was thrown down into a cellar and badly injured, and a man and his donkey were thrown down in Whitton Road, the man breaking one of his legs.

The Curator of the Ipswich Museum, Mr J.E. Taylor, who

was also one of the most objective chroniclers of the earthquake, probably summed up most peoples' feelings when he wrote, "I had never experienced anything like it before ... it was so vivid that I am not likely to forget it. The sensation approached that of nausea."

An interesting sidelight on the events in Ipswich was provided the following day by one of its vicars, the Reverend A. Jeffrey who wrote to *The Suffolk Times & Mercury* as follows:

So far as I am aware, the only other earthquake of which there is any record in the annals of Ipswich took place about two o'clock on the afternoon of Thursday, September 8th 1692, as recorded by the Reverend John Langston, the first minister of Tacket Street Chapel. In this earthquake which was felt throughout the East of England, 1,500 of the inhabitants of Port Royal, in Jamaica, perished, being buried beneath the ruins of their own dwellings. Mr Langston states that the earthquake was preceded by an unusually severe thunderstorm on August 13th. This information is given in the minute book of Tacket Street Chapel which (through the courtesy of Mr T. Conder of Christchurch Street) I happen to have in my possession at the present moment for purposes of research.

Damage and stories of panic and narrow escapes from death were to be found all over Suffolk. At Barham, the Reverend E. Ledger narrowly missed being hit by a falling oak cupboard when his house moved "just as a boat on an otherwise calm sea would when struck by a solitary wave passing underneath it". At Belstead, the roof of a carpenter's shop caved in, half burying the unfortunate man in plaster and debris. The water in two ponds here also overflowed. A sound like that "of a high wind" preceded the severe shaking of a brewery at Boxford which flung bricks down from the walls on to workers and spilt most of the week's production of beer. At Saxmundham, cattle and horses were panicked by the disturbance and ran in terror through the streets of the little town.

From Sudbury, *The Essex Standard* reported a drama in the local church.

The greatest alarm was experienced by the congregation attending morning service at St Peter's Church. Here a double shock was very apparent, and it seemed to the attendants as if the building had been struck by an electric bolt, or was visibly affected by a neighbouring explosion.

Accompanied with an upheaval of the floor and a vibration of the piers, a dull rumbling sound was heard, mixed with the shaking of the casements and a rattling as if stones were falling from the parapet of the nave on to the aisle roof. The congregation rushed to the doors, the Clergy (the Rector, Rev. T.L. Green, and the Curate, the Rev. C.E. Crump) remaining in their places in the Chancel, appealed unsuccessfully to the people to remain where they were.

After a short interval, as the disturbance did not return, some of the people ventured back into the building, and the Clergy attempted to reassure them, and the service was formally concluded. Rumours were rife for the greater part of the morning that there had been an explosion at the Colchester Camp, which had done this great mischief.

It was also reported in the neighbourhood that St Peter's Church had been reduced to ruins, and persons came to the town all day to ascertain whether this was the case.*

Stowmarket similarly suffered damage to local property, and a man working on the Congregational Church was injured by an oak beam thrown down by the vibration.

The most perplexing story, though, came from Nayland, a small community situated virtually on the Suffolk border and less than six miles north of Colchester. Here the shock was reported to be "severe" and the Congregational Church – just like that in Colchester – had its cross and a major part of the spire thrown down. First reports claimed that the whole spire had been destroyed and that it had fallen on a passer-by, killing him instantly. In fact, again in a strikingly similar way

---

* A seventy-six-year-old pensioner, Mr Charles Crisp, who was born and brought up in Sudbury wrote to me about the effects of the shock on his home town as he had heard a lot about it from his mother. Her recollections of "that eventful morning" he described thus: "My mother was ill in bed when the earthquake happened. My grandmother, who was nursing her, had actually gone into town to do some shopping. People everywhere were suddenly scared by a rumbling and shaking and were running out of the shops and houses, and bricks and masonry were falling about. When grandma got back and went upstairs to my mother she found her bed had slithered across the room to the opposite wall. Grandma said whatever had she been doing and she replied, 'I have done nothing. I don't know what has happened.' It was not until later they discovered there had been an earthquake."

to the Lion Walk incident in Colchester, a pedestrian had been narrowly missed by the falling masonry.

The interesting point that the story does raise is in relation to several 'mystery' deaths which were reported in the immediate aftermath of the tragedy. Later accounts were either to ignore these, claim that only injury had occurred – which in several cases was quite true – and in time lead to the erroneous conclusion, repeated in so many statements, that no one at all had died as a result of the earthquake.* I intend to rectify this mistake in the succeeding pages.

---

* The report of The Essex Field Club, for instance, said that while "for destructiveness and wide distribution [the earthquake] has been without parallel in Britain" it was "happily unattended by loss of life." A leader in *The Essex Telegraph* of Saturday, April 26th went even further: "Perhaps even more mysterious than the earthquake itself is the marvellous immunity from injury to person enjoyed by those whose lives were so dangerously imperilled. The fall of a chimney in a gale of wind frequently results in serious loss of life. Yet in this visitation such structures have been levelled by thousands, and the attendant casualties have been of the most trivial character. Christians everywhere will recognise in this the hand of merciful Providence. Our streets, littered for a while with the debris of fallen brickwork, might have been echoing the foot-fall of many a mourner, whose friends and relatives had perished in the convulsion."

7 'The Wave of Death'

One of the most puzzling aspects of the Great English Earthquake is whether or not it was the cause of death. The modern reader, having learned of such widespread damage and terror, would probably find it almost inconceivable that such a phenomenon could have taken place without some loss of life. Yet, as I have indicated, a great number of the contemporary reports are emphatic, in the words of *The Essex Herald*, that "Divine providence has seen fit to refrain from taking a single life": almost too emphatic, in fact, when some of the stories must have been published quite a time before all the details were in.

The disaster was undoubtedly a considerable shock to the equanimity of the Victorians: such things were really unheard of in England and the less fuss made about it, probably many felt, the better. There was no denying that extensive damage had taken place, although as few newspapers reproduced illustrations of any kind the reader was solely dependent on the written word for his descriptions, and consequently it is only in the smaller local Essex papers that one gets the fullest detail of the disaster. The national papers sifted the vast number of reports from all over Southern England and, understandably, because they served a nationwide readership, tended to generalize the overall picture. Amidst this proliferation of news, Essex, although acknowledged as the centre, tended to have the magnitude of its damage at the hands of the earthquake somewhat diminished.

It is only in searching again through the contemporary records as I have done for this book that the full picture emerges. In the light of hindsight, one so clearly sees the predominance of Victorian restraint and calm in the reports; yet this cannot subdue the vivid picture which emerges from the statements of so many of the eyewitnesses when they are all brought together, rather than scattered through different sources as they were at the time. It *was* a time of terror for a great many people, and the destruction experienced over a large area of Essex certainly justified the claim that it looked as if it had been bombarded by cannonfire.

It was not until I had progressed some way with my research into the story of the earthquake that the first real hints began to emerge that possibly – no probably – a person or two had died at the time. Certainly, from among the many people with whom I corresponded and the others who I was in personal touch with, I kept getting the feeling that they believed that there must be some truth in the rumours. Several told me half-remembered stories of talk of a man dying here, and an old lady being frightened to death there. In most instances there was no immediately identifiable location, in others the account was so hazy as to make substantiation virtually impossible. If I was going to make my. history anything like complete, I knew I would either have to prove or eliminate these stories.

Interestingly, in the course of investigating the stories, I came across further eyewitness accounts of the event in Essex, mostly of an intensely human kind and featuring the recollections of a much loved parent or grandparent. A number of these I have included in the second half of this chapter, as they underline further the human element of our story. They came to me by way of letter, telephone call, personal interview or actual handwritten contemporary documents (such as diaries or correspondence) and it is from such items that this book derives so much of its detail.

I propose first, though, to discuss the 'mystery deaths' and what I have been able to establish about them. I should perhaps just explain that I have adopted the title for the chapter from the statement by a group of farm labourers working on the outskirts of Colchester who heard a loud bang and then saw "the passing of a great earth wave from south to north". It was this 'wave' which was to play such a significant part in the lives of all the people we shall discuss in the following pages.

No discussion of death and the earthquake could possibly start anywhere but the little village of Rowhedge, just across the river Colne from Wivenhoe. It was there that the one death which was subsequently authenticated took place, and has since found a place, albeit very sketchily, in a major reference book. The death was that of a small child, and it is reported in *The Guinness Book of Records*, where the earthquake is classified as the worst in British history. The entry reads:

> The East Anglian or Colchester earthquake at 9.18 a.m. on 22nd April 1884 (epicentres Lat.51 48'N., Long.0 53'E., and Lat.51 51'N., Long.0 55'E.) caused damage estimated at £10,000 to 1,200 buildings, and the death of a child at Rowhedge. Langenhoe Church ·was wrecked. Windows and doors were rattled over an area of 53,000 square miles and the shock was felt in Exeter and Ostend, Belgium.

Slight though these details are, and based as they must be on the early newspaper reports, the addition of the death of the child was the first printed mention anywhere. I took up the search in Rowhedge for more specific information.

The village of Rowhedge is a small and attractive group of houses and cottages nestling on the southern shore of the river Colne. It faces across marshy flats towards Wivenhoe, and suffered the impact of the shock simultaneously with the larger community. *The Essex Standard* reported, "Although this area seems to have felt the shock with somewhat less severity than Wivenhoe and several other places, yet much damage has been wrought, and the greatest consternation prevailed among the inhabitants. A miraculous escape or two are reported in this parish."

A fisherman named David Martin, for instance, was carrying water to his cottage when the falling masonry from a chimney fell all around him, actually smashing the bucket from his hands. According to the villagers, the poor man was convinced that fate was against him as only the previous Sunday his wife had died ...

At East Donyland Hall, the home of Mr Havens, both the owner and his wife were in bed when they "severely felt the effects of the earthquake", according to the *Standard*. "All the chimneys but one fell crashing through the roof, and the walls inside the house cracked, while much damage was done by the falling debris, so that later the front had to be temporarily shored up." Mr Havens had immediately leapt from his bed and rushed into his wife's room, afraid that as she was an invalid she might be hit by the falling masonry. Amazingly, hers was the one room in the house to escape real damage ...

Donyland Lodge, another of the fine houses in the district, was also badly battered, and Major Holroyd and his family much alarmed. "The house was rendered temporarily untenantable," the *Standard* reported, "the place being smothered with soot and rubbish, and there being only one room (the kitchen) in which a fire could be lighted."

At Mr Daniells' brewery, the boiler was moved on its foundations and beer spilt from the vats on to a number of workers. Apparently there was free beer for the men thereafter to quieten fluttering nerves!

As at Wivenhoe, men aboard their boats at Rowhedge Quay were toppled over by the upheaval, and some craft lying on the flats were turned on their sides. "Most of the properties along the Quay were more or less damaged, some of them being wrecked. Over seventy-five per cent of the chimneys were thrown down," said the *Standard*.

But it was at the old parsonage that the real drama occurred – and the first death of the earthquake took place. This tall, imposing red brick building which had served as home for generations of clergymen in Rowhedge, had now been turned into a temporary home for local labourers by its owner, Mrs Havens. (The same Mrs Havens who lay in bed with a heart disease at East Donyland Hall and so luckily escaped injury.) At the time of the disturbance, the men had long since gone to work, and only two women were left in the house. In the kitchen, lying on a rug in front of the coal fire was the infant daughter of one of the labourers, John Richer. Her mother was busy washing clothes in the sink. The child was playing happily with a small wooden toy when the shock of the earthquake suddenly jerked the house on its foundation and caused the two big groups of chimneys to fall through the roof. Masonry and soot swept down the chimney shaft, bursting into the kitchen and showering the material along with burning coals over the luckless infant. Before the horrified Mrs Richer, who had herself been thrown against the sink, could move to save the child, it had been buried under the debris.

For several minutes the shrieking mother scrabbled panic-stricken among the rubble to rescue the child – but her efforts were in vain. Little Mary Richer was already dead. She was buried by her sorrowing parents at Colchester Cemetery on the next Saturday, the first, and for many years unrecorded, victim of the disaster.*

Having pieced together this tragic little story, I next turned my attention to Wivenhoe, where, it was thought, no fewer than three deaths had occurred. In the light of the devastation which fell on this village, I was frankly surprised that the number was not more.

Unfortunately, my research here has only enabled me to substantiate one of the reports absolutely, although it is quite possible that a second person died of his injuries shortly afterwards at another place, as you will read. The third has defied all my enquiries and searching through parish records and lists of deaths. I repeat the statements, therefore, as fully as I know them and perhaps some local historian will feel inclined to take my research further and perhaps finally reach a definite conclusion.

The first story has as its most reliable sponsor none other than Lord Alfred Paget, eyewitness to the event from his yacht on the Colne. Writing in *The Times* on Friday, April 25th, Lord Alfred described his experiences in Wivenhoe and concluded, "We feared for dreadful loss of life, but I was relieved to find, as far as I could learn, that one man only had been killed."

This "one man only" was believed to have been an amateur fisherman who was struck by falling masonry in Bath Street,

---

* Another rumour which I heard in Rowhedge maintained that the caretaker at a local school had died as a result of suffering a heart attack brought on by the earthquake. The man, who was said to have been up a ladder repairing the school clock, fell to the ground after the attack and was dead before help could reach him. It was Mr James Maxwell, the headmaster of St Lawrence East Donyland Primary School who cleared up this mystery and showed that, unlike many rumours, there was at least a little truth in it. He said that a Mr Jim Crickmore, an old resident of Rowhedge who died in 1966, had told him that he was an eight-year-old pupil at the school at the time of the shock and could clearly remember the incident with the caretaker. The man had indeed been working on the clock at the moment of shock – he was winding it up – but he had merely been tumbled from the ladder and picked himself up in some amazement after the 'wave' had passed! Although one could not help being slightly disappointed at the revelation, it does not stop the story being another interesting footnote to our history.

and partially buried under debris. Did he die instantly as Lord Alfred might have us believe? Or was he taken to the nearest hospital – which would have been in Colchester – for treatment? There are certainly no indications in local records – but I did come across a story, repeated by several sources, that the man had been a frequent visitor to Wivenhoe, apparently enjoying the angling in the area, and he was thought to have come from the Ardleigh district. This sounded like my best clue.

Ardleigh is about five miles from Wivenhoe by direct road route, and would have been within comfortable walking distance for a healthy man. I therefore made enquiries in Ardleigh and learned that a man did indeed die the day after the earthquake. He was also believed to have been a keen angler. I then turned to the local newspaper files, and in *The Essex Standard* I found the following announcement in the column of Deaths in the issue dated April 26th:

> On April 23rd at Great Horkesley (after a sad accident) John Burbidge of Ardleigh, for many years in the employ of Lord Ashburton, as superintendent of building operations. Aged 55.

The evidence was obviously far from conclusive. I could find no obituary report that might provide further clues. Nor are there now any Burbidges living in the area who might have been able to confirm whether John Burbidge had been the man at Wivenhoe, or that the "sad accident" referred to injury caused by the earthquake. It is an intriguing little puzzle which I am afraid I have to leave for the moment unsolved.

The Essex Standard, did, however, help me prove conclusively the second story of a death at Wivenhoe.

The death occurred at The Ropery, the home of Mr George Browne, the owner of the Wivenhoe Rope Works. Situated on narrow Rope Walk, by the quay, the building was one of the first premises to be struck by the shock. Mr Browne was already out on business by the time of the upheaval and had left his daughter Fanny clearing up the breakfast things when "the ground lifted up as if it was a huge wave, throwing the ceilings down and cracking the walls", according to Miss Browne.

Upstairs in The Ropery, confined to bed with illness, lay Miss Emily Betts, who was just dozing again after a light breakfast. A small, frail lady in her forty-first year, Miss Betts had seemed to be regaining some of her former strength after a comfortable weekend during which she had eaten several hearty meals. The "booming" of the earthquake shocked Miss Betts into wakefulness. The straining and heaving of the house, marked by several cracks which opened up in the ceiling, alarmed her·considerably and led to a recurrence of the stroke which had first confined her to bed.

Downstairs, Fanny Browne regained her feet amidst the debris of the fallen kitchen ceiling and hurried upstairs to her patient. One glance at the white, open-mouthed face of Miss Betts told her enough. She reached for her arm: there was still a pulse, though faint and uneven. She knew a doctor was needed, but, glancing through the window at the destruction which now lay everywhere, wondered what chance there was of getting anyone quickly ...

Such was the story of the lady of Rope Cottage which still survives in the oral folklore of the village. At the time, however, only Miss Betts' heart-attack had found mention in the newspaper reports. Had she not died as the rumours maintained, I wondered?

Perhaps if the reporters of the earthquake had not inadvertently referred to Miss Betts as being Mr Browne's 'housekeeper' the truth would never have come to light. In the May 3rd Issue of *The Essex Standard*, I found the following short letter tucked away at the back of the paper. It was from Miss Fanny Browne who asked that she might be allowed to correct a mistake in "your newspaper's able report" about events at The Ropery. "It is stated," she wrote, "that Miss Betts, the lady whose death was accelerated by the shock – as it was no doubt – was housekeeper to my father, Mr Browne. This is not correct, as she was a near relative, and very dear friend, who has lived with us for several years." In that simple statement lay the proof needed to confirm the death. Miss Betts had died that same Tuesday evening and was buried on Friday.

The third story from the village was certainly the most puzzling of all, although in its stark simplicity was yet another indication of just how terrifying the effects of the earthquake had been on some people. The only published version of the story was by Mr James Jackson, the owner of Wivenhoe Hall, who had had to evacuate himself and his family to London because of the damage their home suffered.

Apart from giving his experiences to several newspapers on the day after the upheaval, Mr Jackson also wrote to *The Essex Weekly News* on May 9th informing readers of the destruction which it had wrought on the whole local area. He had actually spent two days previously touring the area to see for himself, he said, and concluded his letter: "The only serious case of personal injury that I have heard of was that of a woman in my neighbourhood who went mad, practically from the effects of the earthquake, and has now died."

Unfortunately, no amount of research has enabled me to track down this unfortunate soul. There is no record of a death in the local register which tallies with these details, nor could present day residents of the village enlighten me at all. There is really no reason why a man of position such as Mr Jackson should have repeated in print a story he did not believe to be true, and I can only surmise that the woman had to be removed from the area – perhaps to the unfortunately named Eastern Counties Asylum for Idiots in Colchester – where she subsequently died. For all its lack of detail, though, it remains a sad and salutory little tale.

The next death I investigated had very similar undertones, and if anything a still more tragic finale.

The setting was the town of Manningtree on the Essex and Suffolk border which, although a quiet and picturesque place, has had a notorious reputation in Essex, not to mention British history. For it was from Manningtree that the infamous self-appointed 'Witch Finder General', Matthew Hopkins, made his forays during the Civil War, seeking out – for a fee – suspected witches and putting them to torture and death. His cruel and bloody missions, which resulted in the butchery of hundreds of innocent old men and women, have become one of the black spots in English history; and although local legend would have it that Hopkins himself died as a result of being tortured as a suspected witch, the truth is that he breathed his last in bed, of consumption!

The town felt the impact of the earthquake "with some force", according to *The Essex Telegraph* and the biggest drama was probably at the station where a train waiting to leave for Ipswich was considerably shaken and the passengers "tumbled out of it much alarmed". The upheaval also threw the station-master, a Mr Pinner, out of his chair, and, striking his head on a table, he was knocked unconscious. The first frightened passengers who came into his office to enquire what might have happened found him lying on the floor, and several were actually afraid that he might be dead.

The death, though, took place a little distance away at the river Stour. According to the first stories which I heard, the victim had been a girl who had been sitting on the banks of the river and thrown in by the oscillation of the ground. Because she could not swim, and because of the general pandemonium in the town after the earthquake had subsided, her cries went unheeded and she eventually drowned. When I got down to checking the records and files the actual story was somewhat different.

The Essex Weekly News, in fact, provided the only concrete published details and revealed that while a person had died in the river Stour, she was an old woman and she had actually committed suicide. The earthquake had apparently made the woman, named Mary Saunders, "quite upset", said the paper, and she had thrown herself into the river shortly afterwards. The local coroner's report confirmed that the old lady had indeed told several people that she thought the shock was only the forerunner of more terrible things and it had made her despair. Her body had been found in the Stour on the Tuesday afternoon after the tide had receded. It was spotted on a muddy flat by a waterman named James Lucas. In recording a verdict of suicide while the balance of the mind was disturbed, the coroner said he could not help observing that the unfortunate old woman "had undoubtedly been a victim of the frightening tremor which struck our district."

The last death directly attributable to the earthquake occurred at the opposite end of the county, at Southend, on the Thames Estuary. Today a popular spot for trippers and London holidaymakers, Southend was already enjoying considerable tourist trade in the 1880s and boasted a number of top class hotels as well as innumerable smaller premises offering accommodation and board and lodging facilities.

A correspondent of *The Essex Weekly News* described the morning of April 22nd thus:

> The inhabitants of Southend were greatly alarmed by a severe shock. The walls of many houses quivered and threatened to fall. At the Royal Hotel people ran into the streets very frightened at the rumbling and cracking.
>
> At the Hope Hotel on Marine Parade, the landlord, Mr H. Middleton, said the building sustained a shock and he saw the house rock quite six inches from side to side. He said that the floors creaked and the bells rang, much to the alarm of those within.

On the smart Cliff Town Parade, people out walking were actually bowled over in the streets and many items were shaken from shelves in the shops. In several hotels in this vicinity, people at breakfast had their meals spilled into their laps while the walls around them "buckled and shook", said *The Essex Herald.*

On the famous Southend Pier the impact was quite terrifying. *The Essex Chronicle* had a man on the spot who reported (in the third person): "H.B.C., who was at the pier head, says he was very much startled by the whole structure suddenly beginning to sway violently to and fro, so that at first he imagined a large steamer must have struck it alongside. The motion seemed to continued for some minutes."

According to H.B.C., several early morning promenaders were knocked over by the impact "and a fisherman fell from the end of the Pier into the sea." According to persistent rumours, this un-named man was drowned, although H.B.C. gives no indication at all as to what happened to him in his report. Speculation has it that the mysterious angler might have been a Mr John Walters of Braintree who booked into the Hope Hotel on Saturday April 19th intent on a week's holiday and some quiet sea fishing. He went out of his room on the morning of Aprill 22nd with his tackle and was never seen again. Mr Walters left his few items of holiday clothing in his wardrobe and these were never claimed.

Subsequent enquiry by the hotel in Braintree failed to

locate a firm address for Mr Walters; they concluded that this might well have been a false name. So who was he? A local resident told me recently that as a youngster he had heard stories that a body which could not be identified was washed up on the resort's shingle beach on the evening of April 23rd. I was unable to substantiate this story – or that there might be any connection with the missing Mr Walters. It is probably the one possible death caused by the earthquake which we shall never be able to prove or disprove ...

The remainder of this chapter, as I indicated at the beginning, is taken up with personal stories from Essex which were sent to me, or which I collected from diverse sources, during the year in which I was working on this book. Most of them are of a slight nature in the context of the whole story, but they are the kind of human reactions to extraordinary situations which surely help a modern reader identify more easily with what it must have felt like at the time. In some he may even see an action he could well imagine himself taking. They come from all over the county and are included almost in the order in which I received them, rather than in any particular chronology or pattern ...

I was particularly struck with the statement made by the Reverend Thomas Cato, the Vicar of Summerhill, a small parish about a mile and a half from Colchester, as it seemed to mirror the experiences of so many people in the area of impact. He wrote simply and effectively:

> I was sitting at breakfast at twenty minutes past nine, when suddenly a jingling sound was heard, which rapidly developed into a deep underground rolling noise. Our house, which is a large, substantially built one, seemed as if it were falling to pieces. All the bells also began to ring.
>
> I rushed to the staircase to entreat my wife to hurry out of the place, but the staircase seemed to be falling, and I thought the end was at hand.

"The end was at hand" – what strong words for a gentleman of the church to use about an event some others would have us believe barely disturbed the calm of the county, let alone that of the nation!

From the other side of Colchester, at the delightful village of Coggeshill, came a personal report which linked two of the most dramatic occurrences in the district. My informant was Miss Vera Day, whose grandfather had been the village baker, and her mother a young pupil at the local National School for girls which was badly hit by the shock.

Mr Ely's bakehouse at the corner of Bridge Street lost its large chimney which "did considerable damage to the house and alarmed the inmates". While this was happening, Mr Ely's youngest daughter, nine-year-old Alice Ely, was undergoing a frightening experience, for when the earthquake hit the school it caused panic throughout the building. But let Miss Day recount in her own words the events which made such an impression on her mother:

> Her story was that they heard this rumbling noise which sounded like lions' roaring. The young teacher gave one glance out of the window, saw the buildings rocking – and panicked. She flew from the room with the class of girls following.
>
> Alice Ely was among the first, and on reaching the head of the stairs they saw the Headmistress standing at the bottom, holding up her hand and saying, 'Stop!' Those at the front did stop, but not the others coming behind. Consequently all tumbled down.
>
> Alice was dragged out very bruised and shaken, but no bones were broken. She was pushed around in a wheelchair for some time afterwards.

Miss Day's version of the incident differs slightly from the newspaper reports in that they make no mention of the teacher panicking. *The Essex Herald* added that the safety of these, and the other children, was particularly due to a Mr John Clark who lived nearby and was quickly on hand to help the teachers in controlling the frightened children.

At the village's other school, the British School, another tragedy was averted by a quick-thinking teacher who actually locked the exit door, being afraid that the panic-stricken children would certainly have fallen down its steep steps.

Another correspondent from Coggeshall informed me that this was not the only time the village had suffered from an earthquake, and quoted the following interesting passage from *Bufton's Diary* which was reprinted in the Reverend Bryan Dale's *Annals of Coggeshall*:

1692 Sept. 8th being Thursday and the same day that Jacob Cox dyed about 2 o'clock there was an earthquake at Coxall and many towns hereabouts and at London and several other Countries we heard and ye news-letter said it was at ye same time in Holland and ye rest of ye provinces in ye Netherlands – I was in our garret at that time and heard ye house crack and perceived it shake and was afraid it would fall and therefore ran downstairs.

Another school story was sent to me by Mrs Winifred Sach which had been told to her by her father, Mr Edward Sach. In April 1884 he was a seven-year-old pupil at the Congregational Church School at Tiptree, and on the morning of the earthquake, "he said he saw the wall [now gone] outside the window rock backwards and forwards." Mrs Sach went on, "An inkwell in the desk behind him tipped up, spilling ink over his coat. Thinking the boy who sat in the desk behind was playing tricks and was responsible for the upsetting of the inkwell, he turned round and gave him a punch!"

A second amusing case of mistaking the nature of what had really happened was sent to me from Brentwood, a large town on the main Colchester road to London. Here the shock was felt by many people indoors who heard a loud rumbling noise: there were several reports of walls being cracked and household crockery smashed.

The story from here concerned Mrs J. White, the wife of a local builder, who was apparently confined to bed suffering from nervous prostration. "When Mr White, who had been out, returned at about ten o'clock," says the report, "his wife called down to him and begged him to come up quickly and look under her bed. As he appeared in the doorway she told, wide-eyed with fear, that she was sure there was a burglar concealed under there who had raised the bed up by his shoulders!"

Yet another amusing instance reached me from Chelmsford, the impressive county town of Essex, which stands some twenty miles from Colchester on the main London road.

The general picture of events in the town were best summed up by *The East Essex Gazette* which noted, "At Chelmsford the shock was severely felt. Great alarm was caused to the inhabitants, many of whom were under the impression that some terrible explosion of dynamite had taken place."*

It was at the electric light works in Moulsham that the note of humour crept into the otherwise grim event. While many other business premises and factories in the town suffered from the quake, the electric works escaped lightly – because, said the newspapers, the heavy machinery in the plant which was in motion at the time "neutralised the effect of the shock in the establishment, or rather prevented it from being generally noticed". Nevertheless, as *The Essex Telegraph* reported, "The men in the upstairs carpentry department felt their benches trembling so violently that they had to stop working, and a good many articles were thrown on the floor. Not realizing what had happened, they expressed the opinion that 'the men down below ought to be more careful' thinking that the disturbance was the result of the removal of some old buildings then supposed to be going on in the yard."

At the prison on the north side of the town the earthquake nearly provided the means for a mass escape of prisoners. Said *The Essex Standard*, "The massive pile known as Her Majesty's Prison vibrated and seemed to be for a few moments agitated as a vessel would be by the swell of the sea. Fearing that the walls might at any minute split open, releasing the felons inside, the officials all turned out in force to see what was amiss. They were much relieved when no extensive damage to the Prison could be observed."

The signalman at Chelmsford railway station also had a hair-raising few moments when his elevated box "rocked from side to side in an alarming extent" according to an eyewitness. The unfortunate man was flung against the levers which jerked the signals "up and down in a crazy dance", and he was convinced that the whole framework was going to fall.

At the butcher shop belonging to a Mr Gaywood, at the other end of the town, the quake seems to have been less severely felt if we are to believe the hilarious comment the owner is said to have made to one of his customers: "Hullo,

* In a nice piece of journalistic juxtaposition, the *Gazette* carried in an adjoining column to this report an account of the court case in Birmingham where the two 'Dynamiters', Egan and Daly, had been charged with conspiring to cause an explosion likely to endanger life and property. The details have been given in the previous chapter, "Terror Over England".

there's my meat dancing about. Whatever's amiss with it?"

Another amusing story was sent to me from Rochford, a pretty little village mid-way between Chelmsford and Southend. The quake caused only slight damage in the vicinity, but did stop both clocks in the market square. It also interrupted custom in a shoemaker's shop nearby.

At the time of the impact, a man was sitting in the shop while the shoemaker carried out some repairs to the sole of one of his boots. When the walls of the premises began to shake, the man leapt to his feet and, fearing the whole place was about to collapse, hobbled out into the street – wearing only one boot. When the cobbler came back into the shop after the disturbance was over, with the man's other boot, there was no sign of him. Nor was there in the street outside. The customer did not return that day or the next – and although the shoemaker hung the boot up in his window asking that "the man in a hurry" who left on the day of the earthquake should return and claim it, no one ever did!

It was closer to London, in the triangular area formed by Romford, Woodford and Dagenham, that I first began to notice a strange inconsistency in the accounts; people in some places reporting considerable upheaval, while others in the same vicinity hardly noticed anything at all. At Woodford, for instance, many clocks were said to have been stopped "and numbers of people were struck by a feeling of nausea" – while others "expressed amazement at hearing of an earthquake".

In Romford, a local record states, "there was considerable consternation at the local police station." A police sergeant who was making entries in the day book was tipped off his stool and several constables near him fell over. All rushed outside immediately afterwards "expecting to find an explosion close by, but were met with the report that nothing had occurred at all".

Ilford and Barking both felt the shock, too, although here again there were strange 'pockets' where nothing was felt by the inhabitants. Structural damage was caused to properties on one side of Barking High Street and not the other; and while Ilford's *Red Lion* public house lost bottles and glasses, houses nearby were "quite unmoved".

At nearby Walthamstow and Wanstead, only people in bed

appear to have experienced anything. According to a local doctor, Dr George Weller, who was lying down himself at the time, he and others "felt a most peculiar and tremulous undulating motion of the bed". One of his patients apparently sprang out of bed in alarm, and was about to rush out into the street semi-naked when she was restrained by a number of her family who, conversely, had felt nothing at all!

A Dr Cory of Buckhurst Hill also heard similar reports from patients confined to bed – including the story of one lady, Miss Jean Cole, who had her bed moved across the room by the upheaval and felt nothing at all! Considering the destruction we have already learned occurred in the old city and its environs, the letter which Mr Keigwin wrote to *The Essex Standard* on April 25th is all the more astonishong:

On Tuesday morning I was walking round Lexden Park, Colchester, without anything unusual occurring, when on reaching the Church Avenue, I was surprised to see groups of people with startled looks upon their faces. Upon approaching them I was asked if I had felt the shock. I was quite at a loss to understand their meaning, thinking perhaps they had been alarmed by the report of a gun or something of the sort; but when I reached Lexden itself, I found a large crowd assembled in the street gazing upon the Post Office, which was partially unroofed, and then I was told that it was believed there had been an earthquake.

Returning to Colchester by the fields leading to the Union Meadow, I asked some men ploughing in the field whether they had noticed anything unusual. They replied that about half an hour previously they had been greatly alarmed at seeing the whole field move; it stopped the horses, caused the plough to shake violently, and the men to stagger.

On reaching Colchester, I could at once see something terrible had happened; but, Sir to my mind the most remarkable fact is my being almost actually upon the spot without feeling the slightest tremor or movement of the earth.

One or two other correspondents brought to light similar occurrences of this kind in the material they sent me. From the village of Ardleigh, which is less than four miles north-east of Colchester, I received a copy of the statement given to the Essex Field Club by a Mr D.E. Cardinall:

The walls of the room in which we were seemed to undulate just as a large sheet of canvas stretched upon two vertical poles would when struck with a staff. All of us here were shaken rapidly to and fro and from side to side in our chairs, as one would be in a poor railway carriage on a badly laid line. The servants and children upstairs rushed about the rooms in great fright, thinking the house was falling.

My head gardener, who was stooping down by a border, sowing seeds, was alarmed by suddenly hearing a great rattling noise from the greenhouses, and the thunder-like rumble underground, when suddenly the earth seemed to rise under him, and his shadow (for the sun was shining brightly) appeared to sway about and he was nearly thrown off his feet. He quickly recovered himself and ran.

An under-gardener, some 200 yards from him on the other side of the house, *declares he felt nothing and heard nothing.*

This statement becomes all the more remarkable when one learns that two large chimneys at Crockleford Mills, Ardleigh, were thrown down and most local people who were indoors "felt their houses were coming down".

From Frating, even closer to the epicentre of the earthquake, and about three miles east-north-east of Wivenhoe, there came another instance reported by the Reverend O. Fisher to *Nature* Magazine in June 1884. He said that some men hoeing in a field "did not perceive the shock, but felt as if they could not get their hoes to the ground". Yet at Frating Abbey, a house standing close by, and built less than forty years previously, the whole structure was shaken, one chimney thrown down and the others so loosened they had to be supported to stop them falling.

Going further afield to Dunmow, which is approximately twenty miles from Colchester, a statement by the local Vicar, the Reverend A.B. Bingham Wright reveals that,

The shock was felt capriciously; not at all in some houses close to others where it was distinctly experienced. Bells rang in some houses, rumbling sounds were heard, and pictures and glasses were thrown down. The floor of the vicarage was felt to rise and sink as the deck of a ship when it meets the waves. There was a rumbling sound, everything in the room moved, and a lady sitting in a chair was moved up and down. The whole house, which is crazily built, shook and rattled. Yet the shock was not felt at all by the gardener who was in the coach house at the time, not many yards from the house.

A Mr S.W. Poynter, writing to *The Daily News* from Great Wakering on the coast near Shoeburyness, said that although the shock was felt in the vicinity and distinct underground rumblings heard, "pictures and ornaments on the north and south walls of my house were moved, while those on the east and west remained completely at rest."

Apart from the totally differing personal experiences, another phenomenon which caused some debate in succeeding weeks, was the strange vapour which residents in the village of Tillinghmam, close to the coast, maintained they saw immediately after the earthquake. Reporting on the impact in the district, *The East Essex and Halstead Times* said, "Many persons in their houses were so affrighted for a while they could not start from where they were, but when their fears had somewhat subsided most of them rushed out of doors, thinking their homes were about to fall.

"Some persons assert that they perceived the ground to rise nearly two feet and reel from side to side. As soon as the shock had passed a sulphurous vapour was noticed to rise."

This 'sulphurous vapour' occupied the attention of several experts who questioned residents of the village who said they had seen it. They concluded, somewhat scathingly however, that "this 'sulphurous vapour' must have arisen out of their inner consciousness"!

There was an element of the bizarre, too, in the story another correspondent told me about the postwoman of Great Bentley, which is a small community about three and a half miles east of Wivenhoe. This lady was apparently absolutely convinced that what she had experienced was not an earthquake. "It was something like a whirlwind," she had told my informant. "I am sure it was all caused by a peculiar disturbance of the air." And nothing, newspaper reports included, could shake her conviction. The village miller, however, who was at work in his lovely old mill at the time, had no such doubts. "It was an earthquake all right," he said. "The mill was severely shaken and damaged and I wasted no time in running out into the open air!"

At Kelvedon, just under ten miles from Colchester there

was a narrow escape for a labourer who was working down a deep well at the moment of impact. "I was busy shoring up the sides of the well when I heard this great lumbering noise," he told *The Essex Chronicle.* "Everything began to shake and I was sure the walls were about to cave in. I put my hands over my head and closed my eyes. As I waited for it to fall in on me, all I could hear was a ringing sound like the bells of hell."

Luckily, the man's careful attention to his work saved his life for the walls of the well withstood the shock and he was able to scramble up to the surface a few moments later. The "bells of hell" which he had heard proved to be the bells of the local church which had been set swinging by the upheaval.

A group of workmen just down the road from Kelvedon, at Witham, also had a narrow escape, as I learned from a heavily underscored newspaper cutting pasted into an old scrap-book which was lent to me by a local collector. Sadly, there was no hint as to who might have owned the book – for underneath the item was written in ink the intriguing words, "I was one of the workmen and I thought it would kill us." I did manage to establish, though, that the clipping was from *The Essex Standard*:*

The shock was distinctly felt in this town. It was accompanied by a rumbling noise, which lasted about thirty seconds. At the railway station the men in the signal boxes noticed the indicators moving without any apparent cause, and the structures oscillated. The clerks in the goods shed thought that the building was falling.

Some workmen engaged in putting up coals in the yard of Mr H. Smith, coal merchant, were greatly frightened by being almost thrown off their legs and seeing the heap of coals move. Their first thought on recovering from the fright was that the water tower, which stands near, was about to fall.

There was a frightening experience for workers in the silk mills at Braintree, another of Essex's delightful market towns. A writer in the vicinity sent me the report on the event from

---

* Also in this scrapbook was a letter to the same newspaper from one of Witham's most distinguished residents, Sir Charles du Cane of Braxted Park, giving his personal impressions of the earthquake. This letter is reproduced in the Appendix at the end of the book.

The Essex Telegraph, with the comment that it was typical of many peoples' experiences in the district:

> So severely was the shock felt at Messrs. Courtaulds Mills that many of the hands were too much alarmed to continue work, and left the mill for some hours. The Messrs. Courtauld employ some hundreds of hands, including a large number of women and children, and something very nearly approaching a panic occurred.
> The noise followed by the oscillation of the buildings, which are several stories high, led to the fear that one of the boilers had burst, and many of the females rushed to the doors in wild confusion; some fainted, and others went into hysterics, but happily no serious disaster occurred. Many of the hands, however, were so much unnerved that they had to leave off work for several hours.

The little port of Maldon, at the head of the river Blackwater, was also the setting for some personal tales of drama. A local man, Mr E.A. Fitch, who was sitting on the quayside, looking out over the Blackwater, had the extraordinary sensation of seeing two sailing barges sailing *backwards*!

These magnificent vessels, which plied the sea around the eastern coast of Britain carrying various cargoes, were a common sight in Maldon, and several were actually in dock at the time of the upheaval. "As I sat there," said Mr Fitch, "I heard this deep rumbling sound beneath the ground. There were two sailing barges coming down the river, and suddenly they moved some yards back towards the north west without any apparent cause." As he watched in bewilderment, Mr Fitch wondered if they might both have simultaneously struck a sandbank. But when he heard the crash of chimneys and masonry behind him in Maldon, he realized it was no accident.

Making a statement later that day, Mr Fitch also reported that he had heard that the shock had nearly trapped some men working in an oyster pit on New England Island out in the estuary. There were four men in the pit – a shallow excavation on the shore about twenty-five feet square – working in four feet of water. "As they stooped down turning the oysters," he said, "they were suddenly struck by a sensation which made them feel as if they were about to be swallowed up." Mr Fitch added that the shock so alarmed many local fishermen that they were afraid to go out on the river "for days afterwards".

The Stansgate coastguards, who were actually on the water at the time of the earthquake, rowed ashore as quickly as they could, their leader being convinced that a torpedo had exploded somewhere in the vicinity.

The Essex Chronicle presented another personal story by its correspondent in Maldon!

> Strange to say, the effect of the shock seemed to be felt most in what is supposed to be the strongest building in the town, the old Moot Hall. In the police station there, Head Constable Wombwell and PC Parrott were engaged, and were alarmed by a great crash at the back of the building and an apparent upheaval of the whole pile.
>
> They made up their minds that the place was falling about their ears and ran into the High Street, only to see hosts of other people in the same case. The crash was discovered to be the violent colliding of the weights of the town hall clock, which kept in motion for half an hour afterwards.

For a time on the Tuesday, Maldon was thought to be the centre of the devastation, an old lady in the town told me, producing a cutting from *The Essex Telegraph* to substantiate her claim: "The telegraph was kept busy at work throughout the day after the occurrence, messages of enquiry and apprehension as to the possible annihilation of Maldon and the inhabitants thereof being rife." Even a telegram posted up outside his shop by the local newsagent, Mr Poole, informing people of the extent and affects of the shock did not entirely satisfy the people and, said the *Telegraph*, "throughout the town and district everyone seemed terrified by the occurrence and unable for a long time to get over it."*

---

* An amusing little story in this context was sent to me by Mr John B. Gordon, whose mother, Mrs Alice Awmack, was at the Quaker School in Maldon at the time of the shock. "She was woken up by what she thought was a man under her bed pushing the mattress up and down," he said. "She was much too frightened to say anything then, so it was not until breakfast, when the other girls started talking, that she discovered that it had really been an earthquake!"

In something of a contrast, the parish of Birch where I now live – and which is some ten miles from Maldon but less than eight from Wivenhoe – the shock of the earthquake passed with comparatively little impact on property and people.

Far worse injury was, in fact, suffered in the adjoining district of the three Layers – Layer Marney, Layer Breton and Layer de la Haye – and Great and Little Wigborough, where not only were the churches damaged, but a considerable number of houses lost their chimneys and roof tiles, and people and animals were knocked over by the impact.

The Reverend Frederick Watson, in charge of the two Wigborough churches, recorded his impressions in a letter to *The Morning Post*:

I was in my Rectory at Great Wigborough, and happened to be in my dressing room. At first I heard a rumbling noise, and next I was astonished to see some medicine bottles jumping about, and then go into the middle of the room and smash. Then Mrs Watson, who was in the adjoining room, called out to me, 'Here, you had better come out as quick as you possibly can; the whole house is going to pieces'. I can only describe the sensation as being in a boat and going up and down, backwards and forwards.

When I went out to my church, which is close by, I found that two of the pinnacles had fallen off the church tower, which now inclines right over the nave; and I am told by an architect from Colchester that it is not the slightest use to think of spending a penny on it – it must be taken down and rebuilt.

With regard to Little Wigborough Church, which is more off the road, that is perfectly riddled. The body of the church has been separated from the tower, and I cannot think of ever having any more services in it. Altogether there is very great distress in the parish. Within five minutes a parish which was looking a happy and contented parish is turned into one of ruin and desolation.

Today, in the fifteenth-century Little Wigborough Church is the only memorial to the earthquake in Essex – or the whole country for that matter – a brass plaque on the wall of the tower which commemorates the event, and the rebuilding of the church. It reads:

TO THE GLORY OF GOD AND IN AFFECTIONATE MEMORY OF
juliana elizabeth watson the tower of this church was
rebuilt out of a bequest left by the late sophia watson
by the rev frederick watson m.a. rector of the parish
after the earthquake of april 22 1884 IN THE YEARS 1885 & 1886

There are, however, permanent signs of the earthquake to
be seen in this district – though less obvious and by no stretch
of the imagination 'memorials' to it. These are the 'S' shaped
pieces of iron found on the sides of some small houses and
cottages. They were originally bolted on to the facias to
prevent any further cracking after the upheaval and in quite a
number of cases have survived to the present day. (Slight
cracks can also still be found in the walls of some old Essex
churches and buildings which have never been completely
repaired.)

At Layer Breton, which lies between the Wigboroughs and
Birch, the damage was "widespread" according to *The Essex
Chronicle*: "The chimneys of every house in the village are more
or less destroyed ... and the Rectory was considerably
damaged." The parish church itself was rendered so unsafe
that, later, it was felt unwise to continue services there.

Rebuilding beginning on a mansion at Great
Wigborough. (*Illustrated London News*)

Instead they were transferred to a large barn nearby which was affectionately nicknamed 'St Barnabus' by the local people!

The delightfully named parish of Layer de la Haye, to the east, "suffered severely" according to the *Chronicle*. The picturesque church lost its battlements, a portion of the apex of the south aisle and the stone cross at the end of the nave. "Most of the houses in the parish were considerably shaken," added the newspaper, "and many chimney stacks were either rent or thrown down."

At Layer Marney there were fears at first that extensive damage had been caused to the magnificent sixteenth century gatehouse known as Marney Towers. This edifice, consisting of two towers, eight storeys high, has been one of the showpieces of Essex for centuries and is of particular interest to archaeologists, being the first instance of the introduction of the Renaissance to England. Fortunately, detailed inspection showed that the structure had survived the shock with only a long crack over the gateway between the two towers.

But, amazingly, while all this upheaval was going on close by, the parish of Birch escaped almost unharmed. The church which stands at the top of an incline, and has a 110ft spire, was not moved at all. But opposite, on the other side of the road, the Birch School was not quite so lucky, as the entry in the school log book by the headmaster, Mr Joseph Wilkins reveals: "*April 22nd. 1884.* At 9.20 this morning, having just commenced the usual work, experienced very severe shock of earthquake. The room heaved and swayed body, the children being exceedingly alarmed, but beyond cracked walls and ceilings no damage was done to the buildings. The tops of three out of the four chimneys of the opposite cottages [just in front of the church] were, however, shattered and fell upon the roofs which were also damaged."

Mr Wilkins also gave a detailed report of his personal experiences to the Essex Field Club investigators:

The first intimation of the shock was a loud, but peculiar rumbling sound – a something between the report of an explosion or thunder, or rather a combination of the two. This preceded the wave by about one and half seconds, and continued about three seconds, during the latter part of which time I felt the floor heave beneath my feet, and a distinct waving or swaying motion from south to north, very similar to the deck of a vessel heaving with a swell of the sea. There was certainly a repetition of the wave; but whether a third followed I cannot be positive, though I am inclined to believe there was. The duration of the waving was about three seconds, so that the whole duration was seven or seven and a half seconds. I distinctly experienced the effect of slight nausea of which I see others have spoken.

In Birch village a few tiles were shaken from the roofs of one or two of the older cottages, but otherwise the local people were hardly aware that anything really damaging had occurred until the newspaper reports appeared. Then it proved a topic of intense interest both at home, in the streets whenever friends met, and, inevitably, in the small bar of *The Hare and Hounds* public house which stands beside Layer Breton Heath.

It was in this cosy and friendly bar, too, that I first heard tell of the stories of a growing premonition in East Essex during the weeks preceding April 22nd 1884 that something terrible was in the wind ...

8 Portents of Disaster

People will tell you that Essex folk are a particularly superstitious lot, prone to believe stories of old world magic, of cures and curses, and witches, ghosts and 'things that go bump in the night'. Certainly, great areas of the countryside are lonely and barren, turning into dark, mist-covered and mysterious places once night falls. In these surroundings it takes a brave man – particularly on his own – not to see something which tugs at half-submerged fears in his mind; not to think that maybe a dancing shadow could be anything more than just a swaying tree, or a swirling shape simply mist rising from a stagnant pond.

The county is indeed rich with tales of superstition, and folklore researchers like James Wentworth Day and Eric Maple have produced several books and innumerable articles filled with tales of unexplained happenings and dark deeds. Hardly a village fails to boast its own long-standing tradition of this kind, and though too often sceptical visitors have stopped many an old villager in the full flood of some old legend, serious research in the county could still produce a richly rewarding yield.

Essex, not surprisingly, carries the scars of her superstition, perhaps the most famous being the witchcraft persecutions in the sixteenth and seventeenth centuries, when hundreds of old men and women were either tortured or killed in the belief that they were in league with the devil. I myself have written a book on the particular topic, *The Witchcraft Papers: Contemporary Records of the Witchcraft Hysteria in Essex, 1560-1700* (Hale, 1974), in which I brought together a whole variety of documents and reports from the period which clearly illustrated how rampant superstition and bigotry combined to enact a bloody era of evil and death.

It would, however, be unfair to judge the county solely on this period of abberation, and, indeed, during my research I found much to believe that there was goodness and commonsense in abundance. But there was no denying the local peoples' belief in those strange, instinctive insights which it is impossible to define and yet which give us a warning or premonition – even precognition – of things that are to be. Again I found this to be true when working on the history of the earthquake, and I slowly assembled a batch of stories and reports which showed that there were people in Essex who felt there was something in the air in the weeks leading up to April 22nd 1884. We have already studied in Chapter 3 how geographical conditions throughout the world seemed to be presaging disaster in various forms; here we shall see how it was similarly occurring in a human context.

The first hint of this premonition among local people was given in the letter by the redoubtable Vicar of West Mersea, the Reverend T.R. Musselwhite, which we discussed briefly at the end of Chapter 5 about the wrecking of Mersea Island. The vicar had been just one of several people living on the island who had felt a seismic tremor during the early hours of the morning of Monday, February 18th 1884. He had discussed the phenomenon with a friend, Mr Hugh Green, who lived on the Strood, and who had similarly been awakened by the rumbling sound and movement of the ground. It may well have been a joint decision by the two men that the Reverend Musselwhite should send his letter to *The Essex Standard*.

The first body to investigate this aspect of the earthquake was The Essex Field Club, whose membership of laymen, geographers and scientists, did so much in recording details of the upheaval. In their report, which was first presented in the form of an address to members at a meeting on February 28th 1885, and thereafter printed, the leading investigators, Raphael Meldola and William White, devoted several paragraphs to the Mersea incident which I reproduce here in full:

Preceding shocks. – It has been repeatedly observed, that in earthquake districts, a period of great disturbance is often preceded and succeeded by slighter shocks.* There are not

----

* We shall discuss succeeding shocks in Chapter 9 which is devoted to the aftermath of the earthquake.

wanting numerous statements in the present case of such shocks having been experienced, but these are for the most part wanting in confirmation, and are too vague to be admitted in the absence of concurrent testimony. It is, of course, possible that slight shocks may have occurred before the 22nd, and these, owing to the totally strange character of the movement, may have escaped notice, except by one or two of the most observant individuals; but as the circumstances were only put upon record after the great shock of the 22nd, and as no instrumental confirmation was possible, it has been deemed advisable to neglect such statements.

Of premonitory shocks, the only one about which there seems to be no doubt is that of February 18th, which was felt, not only at the coastguard station at West Mersea, but also by many other people throughout the island, as well as by Mr Hugh Green, of Strood Villa, whose house was most seriously damaged by the shock of the 22nd. Mr Green informed the Rev T.R. Musselwhite, of West Mersea Vicarage of this circumstance, on the same day that it happened. On the occasion of our visit to West Mersea, the chief officer of the Coastguard Station, Mr Larman, gave a circumstantial account of this shock, which happened during his watch, at about 1.10 or 1.20 on the morning of February 18th, and was preceded by a loud report, which much puzzled him, as the sky was cloudless, and the idea of a clap of thunder, which at first naturally suggested itself, had to be abandoned. It is most probable that the main axis of the disturbance of the 22nd was the seat of this premonitory shock.

Although the report discusses this earlier shock so dispassionately, Mr Hugh Green had been more than a little concerned about it, and was fully convinced it meant there were likely to be more, and perhaps stronger, disturbances on the way. Apart from talking to the Reverend Musselwhite, he also contacted the local parish officials, suggesting they should take some action, and mentioned his fears to several leading public figures in Colchester. No one, it seems, took any notice, for there were certainly no plans in hand to be implemented when the big blow fell in April.

At nearby Peldon, the daughter of the Rector, the Reverend Carter Hall, had been another local person who had voiced anxiety after the earlier shock. *The Essex Telegraph* reported:

It is a remarkable fact in regard to the effect of the shock at Peldon, that a similar, though slighter shock, occurred exactly two months ago. On that occasion several of the residents of the district were roused from their slumbers at about half-past one in the morning by a subterranean rumbling and oscillation of the buildings. A daughter of the Rector of Peldon, the Rev Carter Hall, is stated to be one of those who experienced the shock on the occasion mentioned, and she had described it as of the same character as the shock felt there on Tuesday, although of a much slighter nature. An extent of the country about two miles in length seems to have been the only area in which the disturbance was noticed.

In fact, this report is slightly innaccurate for the premonitory shock was also felt at Wivenhoe, which is over four miles away. The witness was an oyster merchant, Mr James Heath, who related his experiences to *The Essex Standard*, who in turn made this report:

About six or eight weeks ago, the time is rather uncertain, at about 1.30 a.m. one Monday morning, two or three people living

One of the many shattered cottages at Peldon – from a sketch in *The Illustrated London News*

in the town experienced a peculiar movement and noise while in their beds and although some talk was made during the next day or two of a slight earthquake having occurred in the night, those to whom it was suggested discredited the idea.

Mr James Heath, oyster merchant, drove over to Mersea that same day on business, and found the same thing talked of there, so it seems certain that the earthquake of Tuesday last was a second, and more severe convulsion.

But was it only the second convulsion? Another Wivenhoe resident, Mr James Jackson, the owner of Wivenhoe Hall, and a figure we have cnountered before in this history, had a further incident to report which he mentioned at the same time he was talking about the events on April 22nd: "I may mention," he said, "that three weeks ago, about the same hour, I noticed what I believed to be a slight earth-quake. It was not sufficiently pronounced for me to be certain, although I stated the fact to others at the time, feeling it might be some kind of warning."

In hindsight, it is a little hard to appreciate why these reports by sober and respected people should have been so totally ignored. We know that the Victorian authorities enjoyed a blissful faith in their own immunity from trouble because of the might of their nation, but the way all references to prior warnings about a possible earthquake were dropped from the subsequent official statements, with the exception of that by the Essex Field Club, makes one realize that there were some embarrassed people around. No doubt they felt at the time that tales of an earthquake sounded somewhat unlikely, and, after all, nothing was supposed to be allowed to disturb the calm of English life at this time, was it?

Not that one is now suggesting the earthquake might have been minimised in any way, but if nothing else had been done other than warning the people of Essex of the *possibility* of trouble – by a statement in the press, perhaps – certainly the population might have been less panic-stricken and their houses and buildings prepared in some way for the blow which devastated so many of them.

Two further interesting newspaper cuttings which were sent to me indicate that there might even have been other, and later still, premonitory shocks, though in both cases I have been unable to unearth any further information. I therefore reprint both as they appeared.

The first clipping is from *The Essex Telegraph* of April 26th and states simply, "Although little importance was attached to it at the time, there seems little doubt that a premonitory shock was felt between five and six o'clock on Monday night, many persons thinking it was the rumbling of distant thunder."

The second, and perhaps more intriguing report, comes from Ipswich and, if we are to believe it, indicates that there was a warning of the ultimate earthquake *only half an hour before it happened*. The item is from *The East Anglian Daily Times* of Thursday April 24th:

A correspondent says, 'Mr George Drake, one of the foremen at St Peter's Iron Works (Messrs E.R. and F. Turner) states that during the breakfast hour on Tuesday morning, whilst alone in the pattern-maker's workshop, reading a newspaper, he was conscious of a low rumbling sound and of a tremulous oscillating movement. Becoming seriously alarmed he was about to quit the building in fear of its falling when the motion ceased, after a duration (he thinks) of nearly three minutes, the time being about 8.45. On the occurrence of the shock so generally felt at 9.20 he rushed down to the foundry to see what had happened, and thence to the offices, where he described his experiences of half an hour before.' Our correspondent adds: – 'Contrary to expectation there appears no record in Wednesday's papers of any noise or motion as observed by Drake at 8.45.

It was *The East Anglian Daily Times* which also carried one of the reports of the earthquake being predicted by *astrology*! This science of forecasting the future by the position of the stars was by no means as universally popular then as it is today, but it certainly had its devotees in town and country alike who would have been aware of the import of the letter from a reader signing him (or herself) "W.W.S." of Ipswich:

Sir – Although we know it is said 'Prophesying serve not for them that believe not, but for them which believe' (I Cor.xiv 22), I therefore write, with your kind permission, for those of your readers that may be interested in astrologic art, as was the late Dean Stanley, as is proved in the sermon on the capsizing of the Eurydice during a sudden squall, who said, 'The calamities of this world, so it would seem, come not by accident, but by fixed laws, by a combination of causes, which, on looking back seem irresistible.'

The Ancients say, When you find at the vernal equinox the close proximity of Saturn to the cusp of the fourth house of the heavens in Gemini it pre-signifies earthquakes and high winds in the Western parts, viz., England, London, and the United States &c. This was the position on Thursday, March 20th 1884. The serious earthquake shock in Essex and Suffolk this day is, to say the least, a strange coincidence. Last year we had warning that earthquakes would be felt in the Grecian Archipelago in July, and on July 28th the awful earthquake took place in the Island of Ischia, a few degrees west of the Grecian Archipelago, destroying Casamicciola and more than five thousand lives.

W.W.S.

Ipswich, April 22nd 1884

The editor of the *Daily Times* restrained himself to a single line comment which might not necessarily have been written as light-heartedly as it at first appears: "What a pity W.W.S. did not write last week."

The London *Daily Echo* also carried a reference in its astrological column during the first week of April that during the month "there would be an upheaval in Eastern England of a kind not before experienced." Only *The Essex Telegraph* seems to have recalled – or been reminded – of this prediction, and commented with open-minded fairness: "It is stated that the earthquake was foretold in the *Echo* some three weeks ago, and the people who pin their faith to the adumbrations of almanac-makers will certainly be strengthened by the fact that these authorities predicted some such visitations as that which has caused panic throughout the whole of the Eastern Division of Essex."

The story prompted another reader to write and let the editor know that this was not the first earthquake which Colchester had experienced. He referred to Thomas Cromwell's *History and Description of the Ancient Town of Colchester*, published in 1825, in which a reference is made to St Peter's Church "nearly being thrown down" by an earthquake. The details, said Cromwell, were recorded in the parish register by the Vicar, the Reverend Robert Dickman.

The entry is to the effect that 'on Thursday, September 8th 1692, there happened, about two of the clock in the afternoon, for the space of a minute or more, an universal Earthquake all over England, France, Holland and some parts of Germany. And particularly it was attested to me by the Masons that were then plastering the Steeple of St Peter's in this Town, and upon the uppermost scaffold that the steeple parted so wide in the midst that they could have put their hand into the crack or cleft, and immediately shut up close again, without any damage to the workmen (who expected all would have fallen down) or to the Steeple itself. Most of the houses here and elsewhere shook, and part of a chimney fell down on North-hill; and very many who were sensible of it were taken at the same time with a giddyness in their heads for some short time. In witness of what is here related, I have hereto set my hand, Robert Dickman, Minister of St Pet. Colchester.'

Another Colchester church featured in a sad case of coincidence which I found in the pages of *The Illustrated Police News* of May 3rd 1884 under a column entitled "Passing Notes". It referred to the unfortunate Lion Walk Congregation Church which, as we have already seen, was badly damaged and lost its spire. The report states:

There is a rather curious coincidence in connection with the destruction of the spire of the Lion Walk Congregational Church by the late earthquake. Some thirty or forty years ago where it stood was a queer, ugly octagonal building, called the Round Meeting. The congregation here chose as their minister a brilliant young student, T.W. Davids. After he had preached in this building for many years, the desire grew very strong in him to see a worthier building, and he laboured to obtain one with a zeal and energy that was tireless. He was active during the building, absorbed in every detail of it, and well do we remember his satisfaction and pride in the completion of the work, to which there had been many obstacles of many kinds. The opening of the new building – dedication service, or whatever it was, we forget the name they gave it – was very impressive. The sermon in the morning was preached by the late Samuel Martin, of Westminster, whose silvery hair, deep, earnest eyes, and musical voice gave him advantages that we have heard some of the Dissenting brethren comment on with just a *soupçon* of fox-and-the-grapes contempt. We remember that he preached from the text, 'And the King said unto the prophet Nathan: See now, I dwell in an house of cedar, but the ark of God dwelleth within curtains.' His sermon was an eloquent plea for beautiful architecture for the purpose of religious worship, and the way he brought in that phrase – 'I will dwell in an house of cedar, but the ark of God dwelleth within curtains' – like a chorus, or the refrain of a song, was one of the most effective things I ever heard. Well, in this new 'house of cedar', Mr Davids preached for years. Some time ago his health necessitated his retirement, and only last week he was found in his study – dead. It was only on Monday that I got a newspaper giving an account of his funeral, and on Tuesday morning came the earthquake shock, which toppled down the spire of the church, to the building of which he had given so much of life and energy, and which we laughingly called 'St David's' after him. The spire may be rebuilt; but the generous, warmhearted, kindly human brother, to whom so many young men – now growing grey, some of them – looked, and not in vain, for ready help and sympathy, who stirred them to think and feel, to love what was beautiful and true – he has gone beyond recall. His work, though, remains, and those who caught inspiration from him have become themselves centres of influence.

There was also a second case of coincidence in religious affairs as I discovered in a clipping from *The Essex Herald* of April 28th, which was sent to me. Under the heading "A Curious Coincidence", the newspaper noted: "It is a singular coincidence that the first lesson on the Sunday morning preceding the earthquake in Essex and Suffolk was from *Numbers XVI*, recording the earthquake which swallowed up Korah, Dathan and Abiram."

This particular chapter in the Bible deals with the unavailing efforts of Moses to show Korah, Dathan and Abiram and their followers from among the Israelites the evil of their ways. He therefore calls on the Lord to demonstrate to all the assembled company his power by destroying the wicked men in a manner that all may see. The verses which were particularly emphasized that weekend were 30-32 which read:

30. But if the Lord make a new thing, and the earth open her mouth, and swallow them up, with all that appertain unto them, and they go down quick into the pit; then ye shall understand that these men have provoked the Lord.
31. And it came to pass, as he had made an end of speaking all these words,

that the ground clave asunder that was under them:
32. And the earth opened her mouth, and swallowed them up, and their houses, and all the men that appertained unto Korah, and all their goods.

In the light of what subsequently happened in the county two days later, it is not difficult to imagine the effect remembering those words would have had on the minds of a great many people. Nor is it too much of a surprise to learn, as the next chapter will relate, that the church services held throughout the district later in the week were literally packed out!

The animal world also provided a number of portents which were not lost on the local people. A reader of *The Essex Weekly News* notes a most unusual reaction amongst his bees just prior to the shock. The man, who signed himself 'Paterfamilias' wrote from Maldon on April 23rd:

The following curious fact may perhaps be of interest to some of your agricultural readers: – I was attending to my hives on Tuesday morning at about a quarter past nine, when the bees, which had hitherto been busily working, suddenly ceased, and without apparent reason became torpid. In fact it seemed as though the inhabitants of each hive had been stricken with paralysis.

As I was endeavouring to ascertain the cause of this eccentric behaviour, the earthquake passed, and caused the hive to oscillate very perceptibly for several seconds. After the shock had ceased, the bees slowly recovered consciousness and resumed work.

This is by no means the first instance on record of this extraordinary foreknowledge on the part of bees and kindred insects, for in countries where earthquakes are of frequent occurrence the same thing has often been noticed.

During my enquiries, I also heard it said that local inhabitants had noticed cattle lying down, close together, for several days immediately preceding the shock – another sign to country people that bad weather was in the offing; similarly, that there had been an unnatural absence of fish in all the rivers on Monday 21st, and that no bird-song was heard in many areas on the Tuesday morning until after the earthquake had passed. Another story claimed that not a single cock in the Mersea district had crowed at dawn on the fateful day.

Perhaps, though, the most extraordinary portent, if I may be allowed to call it such, was the incident of the 'exploding' bomb at Colchester Post Office. With all the recent terrorist activities in Northern Ireland and even England itself, there was an eerie poignancy about this story which I found in a corner of *The Essex Telegraph* of April 26th:

A curious incident occurred in the Post Office in Head Street during the sorting of the letters on Tuesday morning, a few hours before the earthquake. When one of the packages sent as a letter was being stamped by an official, there was a sudden explosion, and a hissing stream of fire poured out from it.

Every occupant of the apartment rushed out, and did not venture to return until the danger appeared to be over. An examination of the package showed that it was filled with boxes of matches (*fusée*), one of which had ignited from the concussion caused by the stamping.

The package was addressed to a soldier at the Camp.

The most intriguing portents, and certainly those which caused most attention, were the 'signs in the sky' as they were generally classified – freak weather conditions or actual inexplicable phenomena in the heavens.

The Essex Field Club's study on the earthquake commented on this aspect of the disturbance with these general remarks: "The tendency to connect such unusual and terrible visitation as earthquakes with extraordinary atmospheric phenomena, such as fiery meteors, storms and tempests, etc., has been manifest from the earliest periods and is by no means extinct at the present time."

From its own enquiries it was able to report three such incidents occurring early on the morning of April 22nd. "A report from Lowestoft asserts that 'a remarkable agitation of the water in the New Dock took place, assuming the appearance of a water-spout rising from off the surface – a volume of sand, too, was noticed in a state of gyration'. From Wansford in Northamptonshire, also, an observer states that a whirlwind passed over the field where he was working, and a similar phenomenon was noticed at Tring in Hertforshire."

The Club, though, were not inclined to lay much store by these accounts, adding: "There can be no reason for doubting the fact that on a calm spring morning vorticose movements may suddenly arise in the atmosphere – such phenomena are in fact too common to excite special attention. Looked at in the 'dry light' of Science, however, there is not the slightest reason in the present state of knowledge for connecting these atmospheric movements with the earthquake, except as coincidences.''

Other people, however, were far less inclined to call them 'coincidences'.

The Essex Standard was similarly intrigued by these portents and made a particular reference to them in its leader column on April 26th. The writer, though, was inclined to be more open-minded than the Essex Field Club:

It is a peculiar circumstance, but whether it be a necessary concomitant of earthquakes we must leave men of science to determine, that of late the weather has been peculiar. Various shocks have frequently been accompanied, or rather preceded, by an abnormal state of the atmosphere.

For several days before the late shock, the weather was dull and of a very threatening character. On Tuesday morning there was a heavy shower of rain and sleet as early as five o'clock; but at the time of the shock, the clouds had, for the most part, cleared away, the sun giving the morning that peculiarly fresh and cheerful appearance so often noticed at this time of year.

It was this fact which gave the shock its awe-inspiring aspect, and caused people to attribute the visitation to anything but a subterranean convulsion.

As we have seen through the pages of this book, there were people in Essex and elsewhere who were at first convinced the upheaval had resulted from forces other than an earthquake. The Dynamiters were a favourite source, as was the explosion of a gas works, or the firing of cannon. One man, Charles Fort, believed the entire upheaval had been caused by an *explosion in the sky*.

To this day Charles Fort remains something of an enigma, though his work and principles are promoted and developed by a world-wide group of disciples known as the Fortean Society. His single-minded dedication was to reinterpreting, if not actually disproving, traditional scientific attitudes by collecting and analyzing data on strange phenomena. At his home in New York he assembled 40,000 newspaper clippings on seemingly inexplicable events – poltergeists, rains of frogs, fish, stones, strange lights in the sky, disappearances, levitation and an endless array of other phenomena. He published four books in all, his work being hailed by the great American writer, Ben Hecht, as "making a terrible onslaught upon the accumulated lunacy of fifty centuries. The onslaught will perish; the lunacy will survive, entrenching itself behind the derisive laughter of all good citizens." Others, unequivocably, called him a crank.

Another admirer of Fort, Sam Moskowitz, himself a leading commentator on fantasy and strange happenings, has summarized his position perhaps most accurately, "He was not satisfied with merely documenting the bizarre notices he collected, but offered his own interpretation, displaying a vast and seemingly bottomless resource." Tiffany Thayer, the Secretary of the Fortean Society, put the purpose of Fort's work even more simply, "To make human beings think."

Fort's attention was drawn to the Great English Earthquake as part of his world-wide study of explosions and rumbling noises which he considered had too readily been categorized as earthquakes. He took up the matter in the pages of his book, *New Lands*, which was published in 1923. I can do no better that reproduce in full his argument relative to our earthquake.

> There is a triangular region in England, three points of which appear so often in our data that the region should be specially known to us, and I know it myself as the London Triangle. It is pointed in the north by Worcester and Hereford, in the south by Reading, Berkshire, and in the east by Colchester, Essex. The line between Colchester and Reading runs through London.
>
> Upon Feb. 18, 1884, at West Mersea, near Colchester, a loud report was heart (*Nature*, 53-4). Upon the 22nd of April 1884, centering around Colchester, occurred the severest earthquake in England in the 19th Century. For several columns of description, see the London *Times*, April 23. There is a long list of towns in which there was great damage: in 24 parishes near Colchester, 1,250 buildings were damaged. One of the places that suffered most was West Mersea (*Daily Chronicle*, April 28th).
>
> There was something in the sky, according to G.P. Yeats (*Observations upon the Earthquake of Dec. 17, 1896*, p.6). It was a red

appearance in the sky over Colchester, at the time of the shock of April 22, 1884.

The next day, according to a writer in *Knowledge*, 5-336, a stone fell from the sky, breaking glass in his greenhouse, in Essex. It was a quartz stone, and unlike anything usually known as meteoritic.

The indications, according to my reading of the data, and my impressions of such repeating occurrences as those at Fort Klamath, are that perhaps an explosion occurred in the sky, near Colchester, upon Feb.·18, 1884; that a great explosion did occur over Colchester, upon the 22nd of April, and that a great volume of debris spread over England, in a northwesterly direction, passing over Worcestershire and Shropshire, and continuing on toward Liverpool, nucleating moisture and falling in the blackest of rain. From the Stonyhurst Observatory, near Liverpool, was reported, occurring at 11 a.m. April 26, 'the most extraordinary darkness remembered'; forty minutes later rain 'as black as ink', and then black snow and black hail (*Nature*, 30-6). Black hail fell at Chaigley, several miles from Liverpool (*Stonyhurst Magazine*, 1-267). Five hours later, black substance fell at Crowle, near Worcester (*Nature*, 30-32). Upon the 28th, at Church Stretton and Much Wenlock, Shropshire, fell torrents of liquid like ink and water in equal proportions (*The Field*, May 3, 1884). In the *Jour.Roy.Met.Soc.*, 11-7, it is said that, upon the 28th, half a mile from Lilleshall, Shropshire, an unknown pink substance was brought down by a storm. Upon the 3rd of May, black substance fell again at Crowle (*Nature*, 30-32).

In *Nature*, 30-216, a correspondent writes that, upon June 22, 1884, at Fletching, Sussex, southwest of Colchester, there was intense darkness, and that rain then brought down flakes of soot in such abundance that it seemed to be 'snowing black'. This was several months after the shock at Colchester, but my datum for thinking that another explosion or disturbance of some kind, had occurred in the same local sky, is that, as reported by the inmates of one house, a slight shock was felt, upon the 24th of June at Colchester, showing that the phenomena were continuing. See Roper's *List of Earthquakes*.

Was not the loud report heard upon February 18th probably an explosion in the sky, inasmuch as the sound was great and the quake little? Were not succeeding phenomena sounds and concussions and the fall of debris from explosions in the sky, acceptably upon April 22, and perhaps continuing until the 24th of June? Then where are the circumstances by which one small

The terrible damage suffered by the ancient Langenhoe Parish Church

A view of the destruction wrought inside Langenhoe Church

The Mill House at Fingringhoe where a workman on the roof was thrown down and nearly killed

The devastated Wick Farm at Langenhoe—typical of the damage inflicted on rural properties

New houses and old suffered alike when the earthquake struck
Abberton as this photograph clearly shows

The famous *Peldon Rose* public house which "looked as if it had
been bombarded"

Two Peldon families who were made homeless by the earthquake
stand before their ruined cottages

Another house at Peldon almost torn in half by the upheaval

A view of Went's Mill, Peldon, after the second tragedy to strike this family

Scarcely a tile left on the roof of Little Wigborough Church— which today contains the only memorial plaque to the earthquake

One of the numerous mansions in East Essex which was badly hit—this one was at Great Wigborough

A house at Rowhedge which had to be hastily shored up to prevent it from falling after the disturbance

Workmen at Wivenhoe begin the enormous task of putting right the damage caused by the earthquake

EFFECTS OF
THE EARTHQUAKE IN ESSEX.
APRIL 22ND 1884.

One of the postcards depicting scenes from the earthquake which
was sold to raise funds for the restoration work

part of this earth's surface should be affected by something somewhere else in space?

Such is Charles Fort's remarkable argument – an argument which certainly achieves what he intended: to make human beings think. Typically, also, he propounds no absolute solution to his final question: excepting that one of the major themes of his book is that there are 'new lands' in the skies awaiting discovery as surely as in the past man has found new lands in the distant corners of the earth. These, he believes, could, and do, influence all our lives.

Looking into Fort's claims, I have been unable to find any local confirmation of his reference to "a red appearance in the sky over Colchester", although, as has been indicated from the earlier weather reports, the sky certainly changed its aspect several times in the hours immediately preceding the earthquake, and there are unconfirmed tales of an eclipse of the sun just beforehand. The story about the stone which fell from the sky, however, is verified in local reports, and the reports of 'black rain' are fully substantiated by graphic eyewitness accounts from Stonyhurst Observatory and Fletching in Sussex which were published in *Nature* magazine at the time, (May 1st and July 3rd, 1884).

So, in conclusion, there seems no way to settle Fort's contention that it was an explosion in the sky rather than an earthquake which caused the devastation in Essex. I personally think not, but there are certainly still enough elements of the story left unresolved for further thought and study. What does remain undisputed, however, are the numerous strange signs which portended the Great English Earthquake and which so influenced those who saw them. They will probably always remain as much a mystery as the upheaval itself.

9 Aftermath

The most urgent requirement of the population of Essex after the subsidence of the earthquake seems to have been for news. Their own panic and injury – where it had occurred – taking second place, people in the towns and villages were anxious to know just how widespread the disturbance had been.

As we have already seen, post offices and newsagents were beseiged by customers who clamoured to send telegrams and buy the first issues of newspapers which carried details of the event. In a leader on Thursday, April 24, *The East Anglian Daily Times* caught the atmosphere exactly:

Earthquakes from a journalistic point of view beat anything yet devised. Crimes and tragedies, sermons and charity meetings (never very high journalistically) pale their ineffectual fires when compared with a convulsion of nature, experienced by all, like that which shook the Eastern Counties on Tuesday.

The public exhausted about 5,000 of our early brief slips on Tuesday, since which time telegrams have been raining in upon us, such as – Dovercourt: 'Please send me by first train more *East Anglians.*' Sudbury: 'Please send as many *East Anglians* as possible'. Colchester: 'Send more papers without fail; sold out before eight o'clock.' Harwich: 'Beseiged for *East Anglians*; you did not send half enough.' Woodbridge: 'Send more by next train, great demand.' Ipswich consumed about ten times its usual supply, and other towns in like proportion, Bury being market day, not being satisfied when fifteen times the extra requirements asked by our agent had been sent him.

In fact, the journalistic situation, which is the barometer of popular interest in a given event, may be summed up thus: Our machines commenced running steadily at 3.15 this (Wednesday) morning; have been running incessantly ever since, and at the time of writing are running still. Whether the public will beat us, or we shall beat them, remains to be proved.

None of the local papers, in truth, managed to 'beat the public' as demand rose with each fresh report coming in of upheaval still further afield from the source. *The Essex*

Telegraph reported two days later on April 26th: "Although an army of newsagents were busily selling in the streets, it was absolutely impossible to adequately meet the demand. The crush at our office was so great that purchasers had to pass through the apartment and out into Head Street via a private door." The *Telegraph* could not resist congratulating itself that it had had the first edition available after the event on Tuesday (about four hours later) and "the greater portion of our descriptive report was incorporated in the narratives which appeared on Wednesday in the *Times*, the *Standard*, the *Daily News*, and other London and provincial papers, and in only one instance was the source acknowledged – *The Braintree and Bocking Advertiser.*"

Yet, for all the newspaper coverage, people removed from the scenes of actual devastation were undoubtedly inclined to think the upheaval had been far less than stated by the reports: which, as I have indicated, was in itself a dimunation of the truth. The fact that newspapers carried no photographs to back up their stories was an important factor – but fortunately pictures were taken at the time which help us appreciate the true situation. Two Colchester men, Philip Damant and George Hunt, are much to be thanked for this. They toured East Essex in the wake of the earthquake capturing its impact on the people and their homes.

Today, only a few of these photographs – by now fading sepia prints – are extant; but those which did survive (in the main reproduced in this book) are a tribute to the skill and energy of these two men. Photography was, of course, still very much in its infancy, and both men had to carry their heavy, bulky equipment on their shoulders as they tramped from Colchester through Wivenhoe, Abberton, across Mersea, and back again through the Wigboroughs and Birch – a round trip of almost twenty miles. Their photographs have frozen for all time this remarkable chapter in British history, and one cannot restrain a slight smile at the people posing so dutifully in front of their wrecked homes and local buildings. Dignity was still essential even in the face of such ruin!

Throughout East Essex, in towns and villages, the immediate sights were much the same: a bewildered and often still frightened population out in the streets surveying the damage and huddling together in small groups, talking of their experiences and narrow escapes and wondering what on earth had happened. Debris lay everywhere, shattered houses and cottages met the eye on all sides, and, inside the buildings, possessions painstakingly assembled over a lifetime were found broken and shattered. Many people were obviously homeless – some too dazed to even think of undertaking salvage work among the ruins, others more resourcefully beginning to commandeer barns and out-buildings as temporary accommodation for their families.

Many husbands had hurried home from their work to see that their wives and children were safe, and almost all the local schools had dismissed their pupils for the day so that they could return to their parents. Throughout the district there was much that the young and old alike could do to help.

Perhaps not surprisingly, either, there was considerable anxiety that there might be another tremor. *The Essex Telegraph* commented on this fear, and although attempting to be as reassuring as possible, caught the undertone of concern which undoubtedly existed:

> Although the panic which the shock produced has subsided, there is still much painful apprehension as to a recurrence of the disaster. As the previous earthquake in Colchester happened nearly 200 years ago there seems little ground for anticipating a renewal of such a disquieting visitation.
>
> Still it is impossible altogether to exorcise the spirit of unrest produced by the knowledge – brought home to many for the first time, and practically enforced – that the solid earth beneath our feet is not so solid after all, and that dangers lurk beneath its apparent security which not even the Science which has given us the lightning conductor can avert or mitigate.

The Essex Standard also had something to say on the matter with particular reference to past history: "Naturally enough throughout the day, the unprecedented occurrence was discussed with bated breath, and not a few were apprehensive of a second shock. The aged folk, proudly conscious of their experience, related one or two occurrences which had taken place 'years ago', which were stated at the time to be earthquake shocks, but they candidly admitted that they had never before known of such a fearful upheaving of the earth."

Some of the more practically-minded people took immediate action by removing loose brickwork and tiles, and shoring up any unsafe walls or ceilings. Others decided that the best course was to get as far away from danger as possible. This was particularly true at Wivenhoe where much of the property was in a bad way. One story I heard concerned the Jones family who took to the river in order to avoid any further repercussion. Their son, Christopher Jones, then a young boy of nine, recalled shortly before his death in 1967, that his mother had ordered his father to take him out on a boat on the Colne in case there might be another earthquake. Mr Jones, a relative of the Christopher Jones who skippered the *Mayflower* which took the Pilgrim Fathers to America, said that his mother was convinced there would be more tremors and that 'Divine Providence' might not spare them a second time. They remained out on the boat until late in the afternoon before feeling it was safe to venture ashore again.

Throughout Southern England people watched the ground for any signs of movement, and the slightest bang or loud noise was guaranteed to set nerves, already strained, jangling once more. By lunchtime in the area which had been hardest hit, there was already a rumour flashing from person to person that there would be a second shock "within twelve hours of the first" (*The Essex Telegraph*).

Official records report that no such thing happened: but the press carried several stories to the contrary which are well worth examining.

The East Anglian Daily Times published a letter from an Ipswich doctor who reported that he had felt another tremor during the evening of the same day. The man, Dr H.J. Benham, a well-known and widely respected general practitioner, was renowned for his commonsense and imperturbable nature. On Wednesday morning he wrote down his experience and it was published by the newspaper under the heading, "Another Seismic Wave":

A few minutes after 11 last night, I had just put out the gas, and was about to get into bed, when I felt a vibration of the floor, very similar to that experienced in the morning. Instantly I stood perfectly still, and carefully observed the phenomena.

My bedroom is at the back of the house, looking southwards

towards the station. I noticed that the town was unusually quiet, and I particularly listened for the familiar sounds of heavy vehicles passing down Museum Street. I heard none; but the up-and-down movement of the floor continued.

After a few seconds I heard a distant rumbling, coming as it were from Stoke Hills, and rapidly moving northwards. When at its height the windows suddenly rattled for a few seconds; then it gradually died away, and soon the oscillations ceased. I estimated their duration at about 30 or 40 seconds.

As soon as the movement ceased I struck a light, and found that by my watch, set to Greenwich times, it was 11.8 p.m.

Although my enquiries in Ipswich into this claim failed to produce any further contemporary eyewitness accounts, I did receive confirmation of the integrity of Doctor Benham from old people who remembered his name mentioned by their parents. One man also said he recalled his parents talking about "another little earthquake on the Tuesday evening" but could give no further details.

In Colchester, too, I heard stories of further disturbances, though printed accounts only substantiated one of the reports. This referred to a shock which was said to have been experienced in the town by a number of night workers and "others still too afraid to sleep". Again, it was the *East Anglian Daily Times* which provided the best report in its issues on Thursday, April 24th:

A distinct oscillation of the earth was noticed in Colchester about twenty minutes past two on Wednesday morning. The shock was not at all violent, simply an undulating movement, and as far as can be ascertained in no instance was the havoc of the previous shock of Tuesday morning intensified.

Still several persons noticed the upheaval, and in one instance a bell was rung by the motion. It is probably owing to precautions taken on Tuesday afternoon and evening to remove threatening portions of brickwork and masonry, that further casualties from the second shock did not occur.

Despite the lack of further confirmatory details in the case of both these stories – though there is no reason why we should disbelieve either – there has never been any disputing that strange underground rumblings and slight disturbances of the ground continued to be felt on Mersea Island and in the

Peldon district for many months after the main tremor. Indeed, from my own enquiries in the district, these noises are still heard occasionally today, and although there has never been a recurrence of the upheaval, their intensity has on occasions given cause for some unease among local people.

The Essex Field Club, which carried out so much enquiry into the earthquake, was particularly intrigued by these stories, and the Secretary of the organization, Mr William Cole, was in an ideal position to comment on them since he owned property there and lived on the island from time to time. On September 4th 1884, after months of continued speculation in both the press and local gossip, he decided to go into print in a Field Club report with his authoritative views:

I think the time has arrived to put on record the occurrence of certain mysterious subterranean noises which have been noticed in a district near the axis of disturbance of that notable earthquake on April 22nd this year. The members of my family and myself occasionally reside at cottages close to the coast line of East Mersea and situated about four miles from the village of Peldon, where occurred one of the *maxima* of disturbance.

For some time past my people have heard there on quiet days, and at night, noises apparently coming up from the earth, and resembling in some cases the slamming of a heavy cellar door, and in others the shooting down of a load of coals or stones. During the latter half of August I occupied a room on the ground floor of one of the cottages, and repeatedly at night had opportunities of hearing these noises, and of satisfying myself that they were subterranean, and were not the result of the firing of guns, as might at first be expected. There are no cellars underneath the cottages, and East Mersea is an exceedingly quiet island, separated by a broad estuary from a railway or other source of vibration.

On enquiry of the country folk in the neighbourhood, I found that these subterranean noises were matters of common knowledge, and had often been noticed this year when ploughing the fields – they called them "earth gruntings". I am also informed that at Peldon, which suffered so severely from the earthquake, similar noises have been heard, and that on more than one occasion recently pictures hanging on walls have been misplaced, and articles on tables moved out of position without apparent cause.

The Field Club as a body made no specific comments on their Hon. Secretary's views – though they could hardly dispute them – but they were unconvinced of the Ipswich and Colchester reports. However, there was the report of another tremor in June of the same year, the actuality of which they backed, and which Raphael Meldola noted in his official account of the earthquake. Presenting his report in February 1885, he said,

> With regard to the succeeding shocks which are stated to have occurred, the only account to which credence can be given is that of a slight shock about 5 a.m. on June 24th which has been recorded on the authority of Mr Henry Laver of Colchester. This gentleman, well known as a skilful observer, informed me that he and all the inmates of his house were simultaneously awakened at the time mentioned, and I had the opportunity of verifying this statement by personal inquiry, during the visit of the Essex Field Club to Colchester in August 1884.*

Much as I have come to respect the conscientious work of the Field Club at the time of the disturbance, I think they were wrong to so summarily dismiss the other reports. The eastern part of Essex undoubtedly underwent a period of noticeable upheaval both before and after the earthquake – as did several other places in the world – and I find it understandable, in the general climate of complacency in England at the time, that the people of Colchester and district should have been somewhat concerned about their future; and that they should have turned so quickly and in such large numbers to the church for comfort. *The Essex Telegraph* reported on April 26th:

> It is a subject for congratulation that amid all the perils with. which Colchester, in common with many parts of East Essex, was for a few brief moments on Tuesday environed, the inhabitants were unharmed. It is natural that thanksgiving services for the marvellous imunity from personal injury, and fatal accidents [sic], should have been early thought of. On Tuesday evening – when large numbers of persons were in the streets dreading a

---

* A possible further 'after-shock' is mentioned by Professor Charles Davison in his *A History of British Earthquakes*. Writing on the East Anglian earthquake he has noted that "about a fortnight after April 22nd, a slight shock was reported at Tiptree (near Kelvedon)." He was forced to admit, however, that the story "rested on somewhat scanty evidence".

second shock – a service of thanksgiving was held in St Leonard's Church, The Hythe, and was well-attended. Services were also held on Wednesday evening at St Botolphs Church, and on Thursday evening in the Churches of St Mary-at-the-Walls, St Mary Magdalen, St Peter, St Nicholas and All Saints'. Special services will also be held in most of the Churches and Chapels on Sunday.

The first service, on the Tuesday evening, at St Leonard's was packed out, and apart from thanksgiving that life had been spared, the Rector, the Reverend Dr Manning, expressed particular thanks that the church had escaped serious damage. It was not until later that it was learned that the tower had been severely damaged and would need to be rebuilt at a cost of at least £600.

Speaking on the Thursday evening at a service in St Mary-at-the Walls, the Rector, Reverend J.W. Irvine, took the theme adopted by most of the local clergy, and said that everyone "had been brought face to face, in a moment, with an appalling danger which had imperilled the lives of all, and in which we were made to feel our utter helplessness". He went on,

> Our great buildings rocked and our houses reeled about us, yet we have to thank Almighty God that after so great a convulsion not one was missing – though the town and neighbourhood were covered with the debris of the earth-storm ... Well might we hope and pray that the earthquake of Colchester might be blessed to a far-reaching spiritual good – that we who have been spared might remember our danger, but remember God's mercy more. So would this appalling visitation prove a 'blessing in disguise' – a manifest blessing from the hand of the gracious Father.

Similar addresses were given at St Peter's, St Nicholas and St Mary Magdalen where "the large congregations joined most earnestly in the singing." At All Saints' Church, the Rector, Reverend C. Everett, "specially invited both the communicants, and others, who he hoped would now become so, to Holy Communion on Sunday". A contemporary report says that he concluded by "exhorting his hearers to lose no time in beginning to carry out at once any resolutions that they had formed of the higher purposes in life".

Commenting on the rush to church, *The Essex Telegraph*

said, "It is a noteworthy fact that all the Churches at which thanksgiving services have already been held, were crowded to excess, Churchmen and Nonconformists, uniting their praise for deliverance from a common peril."

On the following Sunday, churches throughout the county were again packed for special services – as were others throughout Southern England where the topic of earthquakes and their part in the Lord's plan for humanity was on the lips of most clergymen and ministers. Some of the preachers used the event as a linchpin on which to hurl stinging reprobation at their recalcitrant flocks, *viz* the Reverend T. Batty, the pastor of Stockwell Chapel:

> It has been said that this event teaches us that God is angry with us, that His wrath was excited by our sins, and that this earthquake was His punishment for the sins of Colchester. We all know that the sins of Colchester are great, and I do not desire to diminish the blackness of the picture which might be drawn of this town and neighbourhood; but we must all see that if this had been intended as a punishment it has been misdirected, since it has fallen upon the steeples of our sanctuaries and upon our schools, and not upon houses which I dare not name, nor on persons who trade upon immorality. The earthquake could not be averted, but the human soul would survive its shock, and would live unhurt amidst the war of elements, the wreck of matter, and the crash of worlds.

In several of the churches close to the epicentre of the shock it was obviously quite impossible to hold services, and the congregations crowded into other places of worship where their ministers assisted in the ceremonial, or else moved into some temporary accommodation suitable for the purpose. In some of the churches in the same district, groups of volunteers had been busy in what spare moments they had clearing up the debris and repairing the superstructure as best they could so that services might still be held. At Colchester, by dint of round-the-clock working, the badly damaged Lion Walk Congregational Church had miraculously been restored enough for a service to take place. The governing body of the church even took a front page advertisement in the April 26th issue of *The Essex Standard* to assure their members that it would be safe to attend:

LION WALK CONGREGATIONAL CHURCH
Colchester

The Deacons and the Management Committee have made special arrangements by which they are able to announce that the SERIOUS DAMAGE to the CHURCH, caused by the recent calamity, will be made

PERFECTLY SAFE

by the removal of such parts of the Spire that might be considered dangerous, so that the USUAL SERVICES will be held

TOMMORROW (SUNDAY)

when sermons will be preached by the
Rev. Professor Cave, B.A.
of Hackney College;
In the Morning at 10.20; Evening at 6.30.

As word of the disaster spread, crowds of sightseers began to descend on eastern Essex, the majority journeying to Colchester first and then spreading out into the countryside. *The Essex Telegraph* devoted a column to this invasion:

On Sunday, as on the previous day, the streets of Colchester were thronged by visitors, curious to view the effects which the earthquake left in its train. In many cases the damage done had been partially repaired, or the debris removed, so that the appearance of the original wreckage had been considerably modified. Nevertheless those thoroughfares where the shock was most severely felt were at times crowded by sightseers.

The majority of strangers who visited Colchester travelled by rail, upwards of 1,000 arriving by the morning down train, and nearly 1,000 from Ipswich and intermediate stations. The strain upon the railway accommodation was so great that an up special had to be despatched to relieve the afternoon train to the Metropolis. Large numbers of persons came by road, in many cases on bicycles and tricycles.

Wivenhoe was the centre to which most of the spectators gravitated, after inspecting Colchester. Here, as in other places in the district, the damage had been partially repaired, and the broken roofs covered with tarpaulin, a precaution which was fully justified by the downpour of rain during Sunday.

The rainstorm, however, hardly deterred the sightseers at all. Many of the local inns and public houses in consequence did tremendous extra business, and not a few inhabitants earned themselves a free pint of beer by retelling highly embellished accounts of the earthquake.

One of the first visitors, apart from the newspapermen, to actually report on the tragedy was the Curator of the Ipswich Museum, Dr J.E. Taylor, who visited the district on the Wednesday. This gentle and objective man wrote in a letter to *Nature*,

> I found Wivenhoe best expressed by the remark, 'It looked as if it had been bombarded'. That was the first idea which rose in my mind. Hardly a house was untouched, inside or out. The streets were full of bricks, mortar and tiles, although with characteristic English tidyness and diligence the terror-stricken inhabitants were already clearing away the debris. Later, crossing the river I made my way through Fingringhoe village and on to Langenhoe. I did not see a single house on the road, large or small, for a distance of about four miles, that had escaped untouched.

Mr G.J. Symons, the publisher of *Symons's Monthly Meterological Magazine*, and a man renowned as being a stickler for accuracy and detail, was also on the scene that same day and was equally emphatic in his summation, "We are not in the habit of employing strong adjectives, they would be out of place in these pages; as, however, during the nineteen years that the *Meteorological Magazine* has been in existence we have had to report the occurrence of several English earthquakes, and never one which could be compared with that of April 22nd 1884, we have called it 'Great' as the only appropriate distinction."

Among these early visitors there was, undoubtedly, a great deal of sympathy for the people of Essex and the disaster they had suffered. But sympathy was not enough. Dr Alexander Wallace of Colchester had already informed the readers of the *Daily News* that "£100,000 will not suffice to make good the losses sustained by the earthquake." Nor was the damage confined to poor peoples' cottages, he said, the larger houses of farmers and professional people, not to mention the halls and mansions of the gentry, all had suffered severely. And not a single penny could be expected from any insurance policy.

The district needed to be designated as a disaster area. A relief fund had to be set in motion. Money must be raised to help all those whose homes and livelihoods had been so shattered. The people of Britain had to be made aware of what had happened.

Fortunately, a group of concerned and influential local dignitaries had already set the wheels in motion ...

It was five local Members of Parliament representing constituencies which had felt the full weight of the earthquake who took the first action to establish an organization for raising relief money.

All the MPs knew the district well – several having long family traditions in the area – and had made inspections of at least some of the damage in the immediate aftermath. Each had received requests for help from his constituents, and their first course of action was to arrange for a deputation to meet the Lord Mayor of London and put to him the case for a national appeal. They decided to include in this party men of different occupations, and from different parts of the region, who could relate their own eyewitness accounts of what had happened.

Beforehand, however, they made their intentions clear in a letter to *The Times* which was published on the morning of April 25th:

PROPOSED NATIONAL SUBSCRIPTION FOR THE RELIEF OF THE EARTHQUAKE SUFFERERS

Sir – Your correspondents' graphic accounts of the disastrous effects caused by the recent earthquake in Essex have made the calamity widely known to the public. But only those who have visited the scene can realise the extent of the damage of destruction which buildings of every description have sustained. Not only in Colchester, but especially in Wivenhoe, Langenhoe, Peldon, Abberton, and other parishes along the River Colne a great number of cottages have been wrecked and rendered untenantable. Many of these belong to their occupiers, who do not possess the necessary means for their restoration. The richer classes throughout the district will be heavily mulcted in the cost of repairing their own property, and though every effort will be made in the county on behalf of the sufferers, there is no doubt that local effort cannot adequately meet the requirements of the case. Under these circumstances, the Lord Mayor has kindly consented to receive a deputation on Saturday, when it is hoped a Mansion House Committee may be formed and subscriptions invited on behalf of the sufferers.

We are, yours faithfully,

J. ROUND   C.H. STRUTT,
R.K. CAUSTON,   W. WILLIS,
O.E. COOPE.

House of Commons, April 24.

The group of men who assembled in the magnificent reception room of the Mansion House on the Saturday morning proved to be a veritable Who's Who of East Essex public figures. As well as the five MPs who had written the *Times* letter, there were two other local members, Sir Henry Tyler and Mr George Courtauld; Mr Alfred Francis, the Mayor of Colchester, and his Town Clerk, Mr Alfred Philbrick; the Rectors of Wivenhoe and Great Wigborough, the Reverends Baillie and Watson; and several local dignitaries including Sir Charles Du Cane, Mr John Bawtree, Mr Samuel Chaplin, Mr R.G. Hoare, Mr James Jackson, Mr Percy Mitford and Mr H.J. Trotter. Also present was the Lord Mayor's Secretary, Mr W.J. Soulsby, who took a full record of the meeting and speeches.

In order to underline the import of their case, the deputation produced as exhibits a selection of the photographs taken of the devastation by Mr Philip Damant.

The proceedings were opened by Sir Charles Du Cane who said that he was leading the deputation in the absence of the High Sherriff of Essex, "to ask for a subscription list to be opened at the Mansion House for the relief of the very numerous sufferers by the shock of earthquake which was sutained throughout the Eastern Counties on Tuesday morning last."

In his opening remarks, Sir Charles outlined the destruction that had been wrought in the region and referred the lord mayor to the photographs before him. "We do not pretend for a moment," he continued, "that the calamity can equal in intensity those that we have read of at Cassomiccola in the island of Ischia, and the still more dreadful one in the island of Java, the recoil of which it is said that we have recently felt in this shock. But still we do think that the calamity, so far as it has gone, has been a very serious one in the extent of the destruction which was affected, though, most fortunately and most wonderfully, I think, unaccompanied by loss of life."

The next speaker after Sir Charles was MP Mr James Round, a member of a long-established and well-known Essex family, who made particular reference to the plight of the local people. "Sir Charles Du Cane," he said, "has placed before your Lordship the fact that there are many, not only landlords, who of course have suffered ruin – that is a small matter, comparatively – but what he wanted to bring before you is that an immense number of cottagers, small occupiers of cottages who own these cottages, have been involved in this exceptional misfortune. The class of persons inhabiting these fishing villages along the Colne ... having a laudable ambition by their exertions to lay by their spare earnings to buy houses for themselves during the earlier portions of their lives – and having done that, in many cases they have not sufficient means to restore their buildings. It is on their behalf that we make this appeal today."

"I will just add," said Mr Round, "that the reports that have appeared in the daily and weekly newspapers are not at all exaggerated. Indeed the reports that have come to us, as representing the Division, have proved to us that the calamity is of a wider extent than was at first expected."

The Mayor of Colchester, Alderman Francis concurred with Mr Round's remarks and noted that "there are few houses in Colchester that have not suffered some damage." He also believed that the local newspaper accounts had not been exaggerated: "In fact, I found matters worse than I expected."

Another MP, Mr Coope, spoke after the mayor and said he had "come fresh from the scene of this great disaster", and gave a vivid description of the effects of the upheaval on the whole Wivenhoe district, "which has all the appearance of having undergone a bombardment."

"I think that this is an occurrence of so exceptional a character," he continued, "that though under ordinary circumstances owners of property are liable for any damage which befalls them on their own property, but still in this instance there are so many cottages owned by small working men who have invested their earnings in them, there is so much damage to Churches, parsonages, voluntary and national schools, which can only be met by public subscriptions, that I cannot help feeling that we owe a deep debt of gratitude to the Lord Mayor, who has been so ready on this, as on all occasions of a like character to meet the general demands of the community, and I am quite sure that the response that will be made by the public to the appeal which he has so kindly assisted in promoting will be of great advantage to the poor sufferers in the neighbourhood of Colchester."

Next, Mr James Jackson of Wivenhoe, said that prior to the meeting he had asked the parish officers in his district to estimate the damage which had been caused "irrespective of the losses by damage to furniture that may have been sustained, or of consequential damage in the way of loss of work or time or injury to health through exposure to the rigours of weather." The sum arrived at was £9,000 and he urged that at least a major part of this be raised quickly so that "the many with whom builders have refused to deal at all till they have money in their pockets may be assisted.".

Other speakers took up the general plight of the district and the urgent need of generous donations for "though it was a calamity general to the whole country, it was the Colchester district that felt it most." (Mr W. Willis MP).

When the lord mayor came to reply to the deputation, reports indicate that he was "visibly moved" by what he had heard.

"I think," he began, "that this is a case certainly which should appeal very strongly to the public. I think the last occasion on which my predecessor appealed to the public was about a rather similar calamity – the earthquake at Ischia, about eight or nine months ago. Well, that was a very sad calamity, and this is a similar one, though as regards loss of life it is not so severe. But at the same time there is this circumstance about it, that Colchester and the district around are comparatively near London, and therefore it is a thing that comes home very much to our own doors.

"Of course in England we have had visitations of different sorts. There may be occasionally a great fire which may be very disastrous, and may leave a large number of people homeless for a time; and there may also be a visitation of cholera; but hitherto we had thought that we were exempt from earthquakes – and that such visitations were confined either to the tropical climes or to climes far south of England. I think it is the first time one has heard of an earthquake in England, beyond very slight shocks – at all events, of an earthquake causing any damage – and I think that consideration ought to weigh with the public in feeling that they ought to respond liberally to the appeal you wish to make to them in regard to those who have been unfortunately visited by this calamity. I need not say I shall have great pleasure in placing this Mansion House at your disposal."

After the lord mayor had been thanked for his remarks a committee was formed among the dignitaries present with Mr James Round as chairman, and it was announced that a number of donations had already been received by people who could not attend the meeting. The indications, said Mr Round at the close of the proceedings, were that a good response might be expected.

Unfortunately, his high hopes were not to be immediately fulfilled.

The Relief Fund Committee called a meeting the following Wednesday when it was reported that donations to date had only reached a total of £1,600. Considerable concern was again expressed about the circumstances of people in the main area of devastation, and a letter was produced from an MP Mr Buchanan of Edinburgh, who had specially visited the area and written that "it was most melancholy to see the plight of the inhabitants, their cottages roofless and affording no protection against the drenching rain."

The Committee barely needed to comment on the fact that the sunny weather before the earthquake had been followed by almost continuous and torrential rain of the kind which had made the previous winter so uncomfortable. As there was no indication of a let up in this terrible weather, they knew funds for repairs were needed most urgently. It was decided that Mr Jackson and Mr A. Ruggles-Brise, who had recently been co-opted on to the committee, be instructed to tour the district and "disperse temporary relief in immediate and urgent cases". It was also decided to call a public meeting in Colchester the following weekend to try and speed up donations.

The Mayor of Colchester, Alderman Francis, presided at this next appeal meeting which was held on Saturday at the large Town Hall. The building was packed with people from all walks of life – numerous local figures, representatives of all the parishes in the district, and as a special guest, the Lord Bishop of St Albans.

Opening the meeting, the mayor said the gathering had been called expressly to speed up general contributions, although he was pleased to report that a number of donations had been received from several outlying Essex districts which, though they had suffered some damage themselves, were anxious that those at the heart of the disturbance should be relieved first. "I am, though," he said, adding the first note of gloom to the proceedings, "very disappointed in the London subscriptions and hope that we shall hear a better report from them."

The Lord Bishop of St Albans, speaking next, said he was glad that the meeting had been called as he believed that the mischief caused by the earthquake had been very great – "far greater than the public has, perhaps, yet apprehended and understood." He then proposed a resolution for adoption by the meeting:

That the recent earthquake in Colchester and the neighbouring parts of this country has been so widely and so seriously destructive to property, and has caused so much distress, as loudly to call for the sympathy of all well-disposed persons; while the sad circumstances demand immediate aid to many of the sufferers of this exceptional calamity.

In seconding the motion, Mr James Round said he had "never entertained the remotest idea that I would at any time have to propose or second a resolution for the relief of those who might suffer from an earthquake in this country." To rousing calls of 'hear, hear', he added, "We must also remember that the district affected is one that has been seriously affected for years past by the depression of the agricultural industry."

Mr James Jackson then reported to the attentive audience

on the enquiry he had conducted with Mr Ruggles-Brise and a Chelmsford surveyor, Mr F. Chancellor, into the actual damage caused. "We did not undertake the task with a light heart," he said, "because we knew there was an immense amount of work before us. Our labours are still by no means complete, and I cannot give any accurate figures as to what the losses will be."

To bring home the personal nature of the tragedy on local people, Mr Jackson read from his notebook some cases into which he and his colleagues had enquired:

"Take No.1 – the case of a widow, aged 45, whose husband died at sea; her savings are invested in a single house, in which she lives. She has three children dependent on her, and takes in lodgers. The damage done to her house is £10. She is penniless, and practically her living is gone until the house is put into a tenantable state.

"Take another case – a woman of 60, whose husband was a sail-maker. Their means were nearly exhausted during his protracted illness, but she has one house left, the rent of which is £18 per year. The house is ruined, £80 being a moderate estimate of the damage. The tenant has left, so that woman is deprived of her rent, and reduced to beggary.

"A case of another type is that of a farmer with whom I had an interview two days ago. His holding is something under 100 acres, and has been in his family over 300 years. When his father died he was seized with the laudable ambition of retaining his holding: he applied his own savings to this object, and, with some borrowed money as well, secured the farm. Everyone knows that the last few years have been scarcely conducive to the financial success of a man in such a position. It is now not a question so much of keeping the farm, but of keeping the roof over his head. The damages he has sustained amount to £40 or £50."

Mr Jackson said he could "multiply cases of this kind almost *ad infinitum*" as they were typical of so many in the district. But it was the response to these plights which worried him, and he added earnestly: "I hope the facts I have stated, when they go forth to the public, will remove the apathy which I cannot help observing in the people of England. The subscription list is not such as I should like to see. It is not such as would have been if this calamity had taken place in Kamstchatka or Timbuctoo – but the calamity being very much nearer home no romantic interest attaches to it."

Amidst applause and a buzz of 'hear, hear', Mr Jackson went on fervently, "The outside public have been apathetic. I miss the names of the rich bankers and philanthropists, which have become familiar through their frequent occurrence on subscription lists for charities which certainly have no better claim on the benevolent than the Earthquake Relief Fund. But I hope when the facts of the case are better known there will be some change in this respect."

Another speaker, Mr R.K. Causton, the MP, said he still believed the public would eventually respond to the appeal, particularly through church collections. Perhaps, he suggested, there might be a better response if people were shown photographs of the places which had been wrecked.

This idea was greeted with murmurs of approval from the packed audience, and Mr Causton went on, "We had a number of interesting photographs brought up to the Mansion House, and we have taken care to distribute them. Some of them are being exhibited at the Stock Exchange and others in the House of Commons. I think if the bankers and those who take an active part in agitating for subscriptions will only have a few photographs in their possession they will the more readily be able to impress the understanding of the people to whom they appeal."

"People have said to me," Mr Causton added, leaning forward to emphasize his point, "they have said, 'Why, it is only a few tiles off!' But when I have shown them the photographs they have exclaimed, 'You don't mean to say it is as bad as that?' I have assured them that it is so, and it has given them quite a different impression of the gravity of the disaster."

The next speaker, Mr C.H. Strutt, another of the signatories to the original *Times* letter, took up the same topic. "I confess," he said, "that at the first moment I thought a letter to the papers would be enough, but I must say we do not seem to have got too much money now, and I think that if we had relied upon a letter to the papers only we should have got an extremely small sum."

Mr Strutt also felt there was another related point which needed airing and hoped it would not hurt anyone's feelings. It was, in fact, the first note of contention that had crept into the aftermath of the tragedy.

"A question I have heard asked," he said "or an objection I have heard raised, is that we ought not to give any money to the Churches, or to the Chapels, or schools, simply on the ground of the conscientious objections of some persons to give to any form of religion which they do not hold. Well, we are not trying to push forward any sort of religious faith which people do not hold, but we are only trying to help the inhabitants of each district, and our own neighbours, to repair the houses in which they worship God. I cannot see myself that there can be anything which any man's conscience can object to in that – but if some do object, I am sure that the Lord Mayor will be only too pleased to put a separate fund apart for those who would rather give only to those who have suffered personally, and not to institutions like Churches and Chapels."

Perhaps surprisingly, Mr Strutt's bone of contention provoked no response from his audience, who seemed satisfied that those who controlled the relief fund purse-strings would take care of any such objections. The next speaker, Dr Manning of St Leonard's Church, Colchester, apparently felt no call to state the church's position and went straight on to mention his concern about the size of donations. He said, "We have heard of large sums, and I am afraid that people will be led to think that only large sums will be acceptable in this case. But I have received 5s. from a Nonconformist at a distance – I have not the slightest idea who it is – towards repairing the damage at St Leonard's, and 3s. from another person for the same purpose, the letter being evidently in a female hand and signed 'From a Friend'. I think that may be an encouragement to others who cannot do as much as these have done at a distance – to do what they can."

As the gathering drew towards its conclusion, another resolution was proposed to the assembly by Mr Charles Page Wood, who called it "very much the pith of our meeting":

That under these circumstances this meeting appeals with confidence to the

*inhabitants of the town and the surrounding parts of this county to support
the Fund by their contributions, and hopes there will be a response to this
appeal.*

Interestingly, the seconder for the proposal was Mr Hugh
Green, the Peldon surgeon whose house had been the most
seriously damaged in that vicinity. Greeted by sympathetic
applause when he stood up, he said, "I am exceedingly glad
that this meeting has been called, because I hope it will be the
means of showing that we are willing to help ourselves, and
that it will create a greater and more extended interest in this
matter than seems to my mind to have been excited up to the
present time. I think we should bear in mind that to a great
extent it must be met by an extended national subscription,
because it falls so heavily upon those who are the owners of
property, and especially the smaller owners, that we could not
relieve the necessities to such an extent without going outside
the district – we should not be able to do it amongst
ourselves."

In the ensuing short discussion before the motion was
passed, Mr Strutt interposed briefly to say that it was the
opinion of the whole Mansion House Committee that the first
charges upon the fund would be for the relief of individual
cases. "It will only be the money left over that will go to other
projects," he said.

A further committee was also set up to "give effect" to Mr
Charles Page Wood's resolution under the chairmanship of
the mayor. They were to particularly investigate means of
raising money aside from the donations, and promote such
schemes "with all vigour". At this the Lord Bishop of St
Alban's proposed a vote of thanks to the mayor and
announced that he was adding a personal donation of £25 to
the 15 guineas which Alderman Francis said he was proposing
to make.

A round of applause broke out around the large hall and
chairs began to be scraped backwards as the audience rose to
leave. A good many probably did not hear the voice of the final
speaker who, attempting to talk above the hubbub, recounted
a scheme he had devised – and by so doing showed the kind of
incentive that was to be crucial in raising enough money to
help the victims of the earthquake. A reporter from *The Essex*

Telegraph did, however, catch the gist of what he said and reported thus:

> Mr John Joslin rose in the body of the Hall to address the meeting, but was imperfectly heard owing to the noise of persons leaving the room. He said: So soon as we had somewhat recovered from the effects of the earthquake shock, and had ascertained that an immense amount of damage had been done, my brother and myself set about making some effort towards procuring subscriptions towards the great distress. Reading the very excellent letter sent to the Editor of the *Times* by our County and Borough Members, and also that sent by Lord Alfred Paget to the same Journal of April 25th, we had copies of these letters printed, and we posted them with a circular letter to many of our wholesale houses of business. The responses to that appeal have been many and liberal, enclosing amounts ranging from half-guineas to five guineas each, and this morning we received a cheque from one firm for £10. The list I hold in my hand amounts in hard cash to £69 17s 6d. – and we hope to receive further amounts, as we do not consider our list complete. We have also had letters from several firms expressing their desire to contribute, and should there be no fund started in their locality, they will forward their subscriptions to us direct.

Although much of the audience had dispersed by the time Mr Joslin finished speaking, those who had heard him clapped enthusiastically, their response being echoed by the members of the Relief Fund Committee still on the platform. There was cause for hope after all, it seemed.

If there was a single word that summed up the nation's seeming indifference to the appeals for financial relief for the earthquake victims, it was disbelief. The very word earthquake was so foreign to British ears that they simply did not believe such a thing could have happened in their midst. Oh, there might have been a tremor – but wholesale destruction? Certainly not!

Following the meeting in Colchester, other similar assemblies were convened in the nearby towns so that the full impact of what had happened might be discussed. The meeting at Chelmsford produced the statement which perhaps best exemplified the attitude of the nation as a whole – a mixture of scepticism and even amusement. It took the form of a letter from a member of the audience to *The Essex Weekly News* which was published in its issue of May 16th and read:

I went to the 'Earthquake Meeting' at Chelmsford last week doubting the reality of such an occurrence as the public scarcely recognised such an astounding disaster so near London; and, in fact, if the Lord Mayor had persuaded his citizens that Wivenhoe and Langenhoe were close to Timbuctoo or Ningpo, heaps and heaps of gold would have been piled on his table.

At the meeting I heard a gentleman mention privately (ladies being present) that he had visited the distressed population beyond Colchester, and the chief complaint was of "the horrid rumblings"; many old women said they "could not get their innards right"; and I presume this was immediately confirmed by a professional gentleman, who stated boldly that he had personally examined 300 cottagers' interiors, all of which were more or less shaky.

Then a gentleman got up and stated that he had been present on the very day in his boat, lobster-catching; that he had witnessed an immense amount of ruin which he could not estimate at less than £200,000, although the chief damage was on the nerves of the inhabitants. Then a gallant sailor got up and related his experience of earthquakes, and how that a Java island had been blown to a distance of seven miles. Then up got a gentleman who began to make a teetotal speech and modestly pretended he could not recollect the name of the jumping Java island, when several faithless people in the audience thought that the whole story might be decided by Local Option.

Then another gentleman gave his experience of earthquakes, and recommended that all Churches, Chapels and chimneys should be built of shavings, as being of a yielding nature, and not liable to be disestablished. In fact, I am still in a haze.

The writer of the letter signed himself 'F.R.G.C.' and although he had supplied his full name and address to the editor, this was not published with his contribution. The following week's newspaper, dated May 23rd, brought nearly a column of enraged replies, condemning F.R.G.C.'s flippancy and disbelief.

Typical of these replies was that of Mr C.M. Handley of Chelmsford who bitterly attacked F.R.G.C. – "whoever he may be". Mr Handley said it was letters like his which still further prevented the public of Great Britain from "recognising such an astounding disaster so near London".

"Your correspondent," Mr Handley went on, "not only doubts the correctness of the statements, but effects to make quite a laugh out of the whole matter.

"It is a pity he did not go to Peldon and Wivenhoe instead of to Chelmsford, and see for himself.

"I would repeat, 'see it yourself' and unless you are 'still in a haze' you will say 'the half was not told you'."

Other writers attacked the editor for even publishing "such a heartless and irresponsible" letter, and a correspondent from Wivenhoe offered to exchange his house with F.R.G.C. – "even if it were twice the size" if he was so sure so little damage had been done. Another man from Colchester offered to give the "disbelieving scribe" a personally conducted tour and make him eat his words – "which should be in fallen bricks and mortar".

F.R.G.C. may well have thought that he had bitten off more than he could chew, for he made no reply to these criticisms in the following weeks; and, indeed, the matter was not raised again in the *Weekly News*. But, as we can see in hindsight, F.R.G.C.'s attitude was shared by many people much further away from the epicentre of the disturbance, and undoubtedly contributed to the general inertia in raising relief money.

Humour was not the only diversion to be obtained from the tragedy, and the people of East Essex also found themselves the object of attention from a number of speculators. *The Essex Telegraph* of May 10th devoted a scathing little column under the title "Improving The Shining Hour" to this topic:

> The unhappy event appears to have set all classes of London speculators upon the move, with a view to obtaining a little pabulum out of the confusion and terror into which the district has been thrown. On the principle enunciated by Mr Arthur Orton – that some men has brains and no money, and others has money and no brains, and that them as has brains and no money must live out of them as has money and no brains – the tactics being employed by those who are deluging Colchester with their papers and suggestions may, perhaps, be justified, but it is to be regretted that any persons should attempt such speculation under the cloak of religion, by creating and pandering to a taste for sensationalism which is only paralleled by the Salvation Army.
>
> On Sunday last, Mr Baxter, who described himself as the editor of the *Christian Herald*, gave three lectures on the recent

earthquake at the Public Hall. We are not sufficiently irreverent to reproduce his description of 'Our Father which art in Heaven'. Suffice it to say that the Lecturer spoke upon the sacred mysteries which no human intellect has yet been able to penetrate, with all the familiarity of a private and confidential companion of the Diety, professing to be acquainted with His motives of action in the past, present and future – again copying the followers of General Booth – he was particularly anxious about the extent of the collection.

Many persons will be of the opinion that Colchester can well dispense with the services of men on such missions bent, and that such services, if desired to be of use, had better be rendered in the Metropolis, where there is fuller scope for such enterprise.

According to a report in *The East Essex and Halstead Times* of the same man "he attempted to show that the late catastrophy was one of a 'series of earthquakes and volcanic eruptions which will ere long destroy all cities according to Scripture prophecy'." The effect on an audience still unnerved by what had happened scarcely requires comment.

Unscrupulous salesmen also descended on the district, vending quack medicines to steady nerves, bogus charms to protect the wearer from any further repetition of the earthquake, and offers of 'get-rich-quick' schemes which could be funded by the relief money the unfortunate householders might expect to receive. Fortune tellers were equally busy among all the uncertainty, as were confidence men of all kinds.

The newspapers, particularly the local weeklies, were full of advertisements offering assistance in one form or another to the smitten population. There were numerous special offers of furniture, bedding and crockery, etc on 'easy terms', and all manner of notices published by builders and architects offering their services in the restoration of damaged property: *viz* this item in *The Essex Standard* of April 16th:

THE RECENT EARTHQUAKE
Horace Darken
Architect and Surveyor

Dilapidations surveyed and valued. Plans, specifications, and Estimates for every description of Buildings or Restorations promptly prepared. Builders' Work measured and valued.
Offices – Bank Buildings, Colchester.

The insurance companies had a field day too, urging the local people to take out cover against accidents. Several even promised protection against damage by further earthquakes, though premiums had to be "subject to discussion". Most prominent amongst all these advertisers was the strangely-named County Hail-Storm Insurance Company who booked space on every front page and claimed to cover against "all the wrath of the elements".

Perhaps in a perverse kind of way, it was the furious activities of all these commercial groups making use of the earthquake which helped bring home to the general public the extent of what had happened. For, once an equal kind of ingenuity was shown in raising money solely for charitable means, the donations began to increase and multiply.

There were, of course, some ingenious, though not always practical, suggestions, like that of Dr Alexander Wallace, the Colchester physician, whose eyewitness account of the upheaval we reproduced earlier in the book. He suggested to the Relief Committee that they might charge visitors who came to look at the ruination:

Hundreds and thousands of curious people are anxious to run down and look at our loss. Already excursions are being organised to take parties round, and there is some idea of the Great Eastern Railway giving facilities to Wivenhoe with the same view. Let us, as enterprising proprietors, turn our properties to good account, and charge visitors for admission to our ruined houses and Churches.

If a few places were left untouched just as they were after the shock for the next three months – say, for instance, Langenhoe and Peldon Churches, Mr Hugh Green's house, the Rose Inn by Strood Mill, the three blocks of cottages, two in a block, a little way distant on the Peldon Road, the new Rectory at Abberton, with a few more suitable buildings at Rowhedge, Wivenhoe and Colchester, so as to give visitors an idea of the real thing – then we might expect during the next three summer months an influx of visitors who would not mind an admission charge to view these results of a real English earthquake.

Photographs also of these and other ruins might be sold for the benefit of the fund, and bricks and stones allowed to be taken away at a charge of one shilling each as relics. In this way not only might a considerable sum be got together to aid the process of restoration, but a much larger interest and sympathy from actual view be diffused far and wide, which must also prove serviceable.

Of Dr Wallace's suggestions, only one was put into widespread use: the sale of photographs as souvenirs and postcards. The excursions were certainly run, but no charge exacted for viewing the buildings, although many visitors did make small gifts to the owners of homes into which they were invited. Fallen masonry also proved impracticable as a souvenir to be sold: there were such huge piles of it in one place after another, that any visitor so inclined could just help himself to whatever he wanted!

In fact, as might be expected, aside from the donations garnered by busy collectors throughout Southern England, pulpit appeals and charity functions proved the best fund raisers. Sales of work, coffee mornings and socials were held from one end of Essex to the other, and there were numerous charity concerts in the bigger towns. The most spectacular of these was a concern held at the New Corn Exchange in Colchester on May 20th, which included several well-known actors and actresses who gave their services free, the highly-vaunted All Saints' Choral Class from Colchester and the resounding Band of the Norfolk Regiment.

Altogether, after its slow start, in the two months following the earthquake, nearly £10,000 was raised by the Mansion House Committee and distributed for the repair of local property. This sum was, of course, very substantially augmented by the amounts spent by local landlords, the gentry, church officials and the owners of factories, shops and public houses, in repairing their premises. Although it would be impossible to put a final cost on the ravages of the Great English Earthquake, the present view is that it can have been very little short of £100,000.

This figure is shared to a degree by *The Essex Telegraph*, but the paper was quick to point out in a leader some weeks after the event that, "Probably the full effect of the disaster upon the various buildings of the district will never be known. But it is safe to assume that many structures have been weakened at their foundations, although the mischief is not apparent to the human eye, and they will not call on the exchequer for repairs for some time."

The ability, or otherwise, of the buildings in eastern Essex to withstand the shock of the earthquake, was, in fact, a topic of some discussion in the press in succeeding weeks, spearheaded by a letter to *The Essex Standard* by an architect, Mr Philip Brannon of Walton-on-the-Naze. He wrote on May 3rd:

> The widespread destruction, or, we might say, shaking down of chimneys, spires, and other buildings, is a severe reproof against the slovenly style of modern building – the rotten and incoherent mortar too generally employed, and the unscientific construction universally prevalent.
>
> Those who are acquainted with my labours are well aware that in the improvements on construction I invented, and to some degree introduced, it was not against fire and insanitary work only I directed my exertions, but against the destructive action of earthquakes, as a building constructed as it should be ought to rock to and fro to a far wider angle of oscillation than in any in the recent earthquake – without the least danger.
>
> It was because the simplest possible law of construction was neglected in the Tay Bridge that it blew down – and had this earthquake been a little more violent and widely spread, the destruction of bridges as well as houses would have inflicted on England a greater loss than any calamity in the whole history of her existence. Trusting this note of warning may remind your readers that this earthquake, like all Divine visitations, has a grand practical teaching, and if we learn from it, will become to us a blessing.

As I intimated at the very start of this book, the earthquake was indeed to shatter the complacency of the Victorian world. Its impact on men and property disturbed irrevocably a calm self-satisfaction, and caused the people of Britain to re-examine some of their most dearly held attitudes and opinions. For this reason, if for no other, some good did come out of the disaster.

The Spectator magazine, then as now one of the most respected weekly journals, was the only publication to immediately appreciate the implications of what had happened, as it demonstrated in an article published on April 26th. First briefly summarizing the damage the earthquake had caused – and noting that "even in parts of London the shock caused great alarm" – the anonymous scribe went on:

There is probably nothing on which Englishmen pride themselves more than their firmness and stability of mind, but firmness and stability are just the qualities which liability to earthquakes most undermines. 'From our earliest years' says one of the best writers on earthquakes, 'we have been accustomed to consider the soil underneath our feet as firm and immovable' – so much so, indeed, that this is the only kind of property which English law emphatically calls *real* – 'we have unconsciously connected this idea with all our conceptions, feelings, and actions; and it thus becomes the base of all our plans, intentions, and wishes. Our whole life, with all its events and operations, rests on this idea as an immutable foundation. An earthquake, by turning it into a delusion, overthrows our whole system of thinking and acting.'

We think it might be safely predicted that as the force of the English character consists in great measure in its strong hold of the visible – in the tenacity and vigour with which it incorporates and identifies its physcial work and moral duties – that any rude shaking of confidence in the physical basis of life would do even more to unman the ordinary Englishman that it would do even to unman the ordinary Asiatic or the ordinary Celt.

So the occurrence of occasional reminders that the visible frame of things is not so permanent as we sometimes think it, might well have the effect of turning our minds away from too great identification of ourselves with things visible by which we spoil ourselves even for the due use of the visible universe. However little there is in us of the foresight of the spirit, we are surely capable of a much further sight than we ever exercise; and the striking lesson we have received of the temporaryness of the framework of our visible world, may give our hearts an impulse in the right direction – the direction in which, recently at least, we have certainly *not* been going.

Those prophetic words mirrored exactly the re-thinking which was subsequently to go on among people in all walks of life. England, and indeed the whole of Britain, would never be quite the same again after that April morning in 1884.

The last question which we have to consider in this book is what caused the earthquake, and, relative to that, how long did the disturbance last?

The study of seismology and earthquakes in general was at a fairly rudimentary stage in 1884 and the lack of measuring equipment has deprived us of the data which has made the study of later upheavals so much simpler and more rewarding. Yet, thanks in the main to the members of The Essex Field Club and their correspondents, who collected as many facts and as much information as possible at the time, it is at least possible to present one or two viewpoints if not an actual scientific conclusion.

The Essex Field Club was itself only four years old when the earthquake occurred. It had been formed to "study and investigate the natural history, geology and pre-historic archaeology of the county" and had a membership of specialists and laymen who were spread across the county. By early 1884 it had organized a number of study walks, helped defeat plans for development within the bounds of Epping Forest – the county's major woodland tract – and published several studies including one on the ancient camp in Epping Forest known as Amesbury banks, which has a history extending back to the days of Queen Boadicea. It was a lively, energetic body, not so serious as to totally lack a sense of humour, as the publication of an amusing pamphlet, "A Day's Elephant Hunting in Essex" clearly showed.

Surprisingly, after the earthquake, the Club was the only scientific group to study the occurrence in detail. Short reports were published by other groups – including the Northamptonshire Natural History Society, the Norfolk and Norwich Naturalists Society and the splendidly named Devonshire Association for the Advancement of Science, Literature and Art – but they added very little to what the newspapers had reported. This lack of interest by others was one of the facts deplored by the man who co-ordinated the Field Club report, Professor Raphael Meldola FCS, who wrote, "The absence of record on the part of local societies is certainly to be deplored, as accurate observations from those counties contiguous to our own, such as Suffolk and Cambridge, were especially required."

Nonetheless, the Essex members flung themselves enthusiastically into the task of collecting information from all over the county – interviewing victims, studying the damage to houses and buildings, and investigating the geological strata of the area. At their head was the dedicated Professor Meldola, a Vice-President of the Club and Professor of

Chemistry at Finsbury Technical College in London. Apart from an insatiable curiosity about geological phenomena, he had a personal reason for being so interested as it was one of his forbears, a Raphael Meldola of Bayonne, who had published the only account of the prolonged earthquake at Leghorn in France in 1741. Professor Meldola was assisted by another committee member, Mr William White, a member of the Geologists' Association and a specialist in rock strata. With their team of helpers they built up perhaps the nearest thing to a comprehensive study of the event, which Professor Meldola delivered as an address to a packed gathering of members on February 28th 1885.

The professor said that he had instituted the enquiry immediately after the occurrence by contacting members in varying parts of the county, and also by drawing up a list of questions to be answered by the general public which was published in the local papers. The ten questions were:

1. Whether the disturbance was violent or slight in your neighbourhood.
2. If any sounds premonitory to or accompanying the shock were heard, and their nature.
3. Atmospheric conditions, temperature, barometric readings.
4. In the case of stoppage of clocks, the exact times and direction of swing of pendulum and of pictures or other suspended objects (bearings of the walls, &c.)
5. Whether sufficiently forcible to set bells ringing or to dislodge articles of furniture, open doors &c.
6. Duration of the oscillation in seconds, if noted (as approximately as possible), and whether more than one shock.
7. Did any shower follow the earthquake, or was any special wind current noticed?
8. Full details as to effect upon springs.
9. In the case of dislocation of walls and chimneys, the direction of fall or twist.
10. The superficial geology so far as known.

As a result of this questionaire, Professor Meldola received a "large accumulation of notes, letters and newspaper cuttings" which he was able to augment with the data collected by Club members.* He went over the district himself "taking notes, measurements and collecting all other information bearing upon this which is certainly the most serious earthquake that has been recorded in Britain". Among the people who accompanied him on his tour of 'detection' were a Mr T.V. Holmes, the President of the Club, and, appropriately, a Mr J. Watson from Wivenhoe!

The professor said his task was made easier by the enthusiastic response of people to placing the facts on record – and by the improvement in communications. As he wrote in his report, "In striking contrast with those earthquakes by which Britain was visited in early times, and of which the tale travelled but slowly through the land, increased in exaggeration, and becoming largely mixed with superstitious embellishment as the news spreads from town to town, the occurrence of the present shock was made known and many of the details made public throughout the country in the evening papers of the day of the disaster."

Based on the data which he had collected, Professor Meldola said that the earthquake had affected a mean area of 52,828 miles, and taking the Lisbon earthquake as a major, or first class, disturbance, the East Anglian occurrence could be classified "intermediate between the 2nd and 3rd class". He said that the event took place during a period of general seismic activity throughout the world and mentioned numerous instances including the terrible devastation on the island of Krakatoa in 1883. He also made reference to the unsettled weather conditons of the previous months, but was unconvinced that there was any reason "for connecting these atmospheric movements with the earthquake, except as coincidences".

Professor Meldola then moved on to the nature and duration of the movement. If, he said, it had been possible to trace the movement on a series of seismographic plates – "we should no doubt have seen the gradually commencing tremor increasing in amplitude and complexity till the 'shock' and

* Professor Meldola actually received 321 replies: the largest being 109 from Essex and 48 from Middlesex. Among the dozens from other counties were some from as far as Cheshire, Somerset and Kent, not to mention five from France and Belgium.

destruction occurred, and then again dying gradually out.''
The duration was a matter of considerable controversy
primarily because of the subjectiveness of personal judgement
and the way in which different buildings oscillated for
different lengths of time. The professor cited various estimates
he had received from different parts of East Anglia to illustrate
what he meant: Colchester 8 to 10 seconds; Langenhoe not
less than 20 seconds; Chelmsford about 5 seconds; Halstead 2
seconds; Ipswich 3 to 10 seconds; Norwich not exceeding 10
seconds and Southall, Middlesex 10 to 15 seconds. He said he
had discounted altogether claims that it had lasted for up to
half a minute, and because of the unreliability of all the
statements he was not prepared to even advance an
approximate time of duration.*

It was on the matter of the number of shocks that had
occurred, however, which caused Professor Meldola to most
surprise his audience.

"The evidence appears sufficiently conclusive," he said,
"that more than one 'shock' (not in the sense of an oscillation)
was felt in the area of damage, and of the various records
which appear in the report I am disposed to attach the most
weight to the statement of Mr Larman, the chief officer of the
Coastguard Station at West Mersea, who gave us a very
distinct account of his having experienced two shocks, each
preceded by a report, the first being the stronger and louder.
It is possible that the first was the direct shock and the second
a reflection of it. Beyond the area of damage, and especially at
the remote stations, there are numerous records of two distinct
shocks having been felt. This is the case, for instance at
Cheltenham, Leamington, West Haddon, Market
Harborough, Dover and in London.''

Professor Meldola felt unable "in the present state of
seismological science" to attempt an explanation of this,
although he personally favoured the theory that as there were
two major differing stratas of rocks underlying the area, these
would conduct the earthquake 'wave' at different speeds, the

---

* During the course of writing his book, *A History of British Earthquakes*, in 1924,
Professor Charles Davison, the Cambridge geologist, re-examined the evidence as
to the actual time of the earthquake and pronounced his belief that "the mean
duration of the whole shock was 5.3 seconds.''

one naturally going faster than the other. (*Nature* magazine was also inclined to this view as we shall read later.)

He had also been interested in the sounds connected with the disturbance. "The accounts," he told his listeners, "are on the whole concordant that a subterranean rumbling noise preceded the actual shock; in one or two instances only is the noise said to have accompanied the shock. There is no doubt that in some cases, and especially within the area of structural damage, the sound of the earthquake disturbance was inextricably blended with the crash of falling masonry and the rattle and jar of houses.

"One noteworthy feature is the statement, repeated by a few of the observers who were indoors at the time, that the noise appeared to break in the first place overhead. This would seem to indicate that the amplitude of vibration of the upper part of the buildings had become sufficient to cause windows, furniture, etc., to rattle before the vibrations of the lower storeys had become of sufficient amplitude to make themselves felt to the inmates."

In concluding his remarks, he said that the shock "probably" originated beneath the villages of Abberton and Peldon and "apparently suffered a considerable amount of reflection at Wivenhoe". He did not think its distribution had been influenced by any known lines of geographical faulting, though "the main axis of destruction may possibly correspond in its direction with that of known lines of disturbance in the Chalk underlying Essex, Cambridgeshire, Suffolk, and, across the Thames, in Kent, but the evidence of such parallelism is not at present conclusive."

He felt, therefore, it was impossible to give an exact cause for the remarkable disturbance, and added finally, "The effects produced could have resulted from the rupture of deep-seated rocks under strain or pressure, such as the sudden production or extension of a line of faulting."

Such was the inconclusive findings of The Essex Field Club: after months of patient and painstaking work, the mystery of the earthquake remained.

When the report of the meeting appeared in book form later in the year, Professor Meldola added, as an Appendix, the verdict of Mr Horace B. Woodward, of the Geological Survey:

"Probably we shall not be far wrong if we attribute the recent earthquake in Essex to one or more subterranean rents produced by shrinkage, which led to no material shifting of the rocks, and which, owing to the tenacious nature of the subsoil at Colchester, chiefly London Clay, did not manifest itself in any conspicuous manner at the surface." It was obviously a sentiment with which the Professor found himself in sympathy.

Nature magazine had carried an earlier speculative article about the cause of the earthquake in its issue of May 1st 1884. (It could hardly have been a more appropriate issue as it also contained the first detailed examination of the Krakatoa eruption.) The author was one of the foremost geologists of his day, Professor W. Topley, who included with his survey a specially drawn map of the area and a cross-section of the geological strata to illustrate his remarks (see below). Professor Topley wrote,

> The shock was most severely felt near the north shore of the estuary of the Blackwater, and for about six miles inland to the north, in the direction of Colchester. The geology of this district is simple. Nearly all the country is occupied by London Clay; over the marshy land of the Colne, and the flats separating Mersea Island from the mainland, there is a covering of recent alluvial deposits; over parts of the higher land of Mersea Island there are patches, from a quarter of a square mile to one square mile in area, of Glacial gravel, the remnants of a great sheet of similar material which once overspread the London Clay and joined the large area of similar gravel near Colchester. This town is mostly built on gravel, which rises to a greater height and occurs in considerable thickness, to the south west of the town. Underlying the whole of the Tertiary beds of the East of England there is a continuous bed of chalk from 600 to 1,000 more feet in thickness.

A cross-section of the geological formation of England from Bristol to Harwich as referred to by Professor W. Topley. Figure 1 indicates Palaeozoia Rocks (Carboniferous and older), 2 Permian to Upper Greensand, and 3 Chalk

Below the chalk there is a bed of Gault Clay of varying thickness, and below these Palaeozoic rocks.

He went on with the nub of his belief:

One of the most interesting questions connected with the earthquake is to ascertain whether there is any relation between the known range of the quake and the old or Palaeozoic rocks which underlie the area. The shock was plainly felt at Bristol, Wolverhampton, Birmingham and Leicester – all places on or near to the outcrop of the older rocks. It seems therefore likely that the wider and more general range of the earthquake is connected with the range of the Palaeozoic rocks – but the local phenomenon also depended very largely on the nature and thickness of the Secondary and Tertiary rocks.

Professor Topley also commented on the accompanying sounds to the earthquake which so fascinated Professor Meldola: "Some observers speak decidedly of two distinct shocks," he wrote, "this probably was the case frequently, though seldom noticed. The explanation for this may well be that the first shock would be that travelling quickly through the hard Palaeozoic rocks, the second that propagated more slowly through the softer, overlying newer rocks."

The professor did not conclude his essay on May 1st, but left it for another two weeks for further enquiries before placing his final summary on record. He wrote,

There can now be little doubt that the origin of the shock was vertically under West Mersea or thereabouts, and the 'wave' must have travelled in all directions away from the area, but not necessarily with equal force and rapidity in all directions. The observations as to the direction of motion generally agree with this view; but in the neighbourhood of London there are some curious differences. The observations in London generally give an east and west direction, whereas some of the north side of London appear to point to a more north and south direction.

The direction of the earthquake was not the only puzzle which exercised readers of *Nature* (they quite failed to find a direction which all the evidence supported) for there was some discussion of the strange phenomenon of the rising water.

It had been reported in the aftermath of the shock that it had "produced a marked and permanent change in the level of underground waters in the district". At Colchester Waterworks, for instance, it was said that prior to the earthquake the water level had gradually been sinking and the management committee had decided that a lengthening of the suction pipes would be necessary. Yet immediately after the upheaval, the Borough Surveyor, Mr Charles Clegg found that the level had risen again nearly $7\frac{1}{2}$ feet! Other wells in the vicinity had been similarly affected.

The subject was taken up with alacrity in the columns of *Nature* by a Mr C.E. De Rance, the Secretary to the Underground Water Committee of the British Association. This "marked change" had been noted in wells from Broadstairs to Bristol and Spilsby to Ryde, he said, and the rise in levels had varied from between 20 inches to the record $7\frac{1}{2}$ feet at Colchester.

Mr De Rance believed that the reason for this was that "the shock has caused a widening of the fissures through which the water circulates in its course down to the lower chalk beds, and thus, by an increased flow, has given rise to a general increase in level in these waterbearing beds from which the wells derive their supply." Although many experts expected the water levels to sink quickly to their previous levels, there was no such drop even with the added requirements placed on the wells by a dry summer.

In the weeks after the earthquake, the newspapers published several theories by expert and laymen alike as to the cause of the earthquake.

The more imaginative, like 'C.S.' writing to *The Essex Telegraph*, were inclined to proscribe it as a "manifestation of the ever-wakeful energies of subterranean fires", while the religious felt it was "the hand of Divine Providence punishing the wicked."

Perhaps the most ingenious was the view of Olivier Borbeau who wrote from Thorrington, Essex, to *The Essex Standard* on May 3rd:

Imagine a huge cauldron filled with matter in gaseous form, with an aperture or outlet. Suppose, also, that at a given moment this outlet is not sufficient for the escape of the confined gases, or that it is blocked up. The pressure on the sides of the cauldron will thus become enormous, and if the imprisoned gases can find a fissure, they will naturally make their escape by it.

The same thing happens in the interior of the earth. The gases produced by matter in an ignited state, finding no means of outlet sufficiently large, exert themselves upon the line of least resistance and in this way the earthquake is produced. The gases force their way through the subterranean cavities, which they find or make for themselves, causing the trembling movement of the earth.

Whence came the wave-like undulations? They are caused by the distance from the surface of the earth to the channel followed by the gases being more or less great, and the gases raise the surface of the earth more or less in proportion to its thickness.

What produces the noise of the earthquake? It is probably this: If you inject into a metal tube of great resistance a current of vapour of great force, and place your ear close to the tube, you will hear on a small scale the same noise which you heard on Tuesday. Multiply indefinitely the force of the gases which exist beneath the earth's surface, and you will have the sound of an earthquake.

But sound commonsense mixed with reassurance was what the people of East Anglia most needed in the aftermath of their tragedy. And perhaps no one supplied this with more conviction than the kindly and perceptive Dr J.E. Taylor, the Ipswich Museum Curator, who, as we have seen, made an immediate personal study of the event. The letter which he thereafter wrote was given pride-of-place prominence in all the local papers the following morning. He wrote,

My personal experience is that the earthquake shock of yesterday morning is much more likely to impress peoples' minds with a vivid idea of the nature of these phenomena than any number of lectures on the subject. Those who experienced the sensation will not be likely to forget it, for although the oscillations were slight in comparison with those experienced in earthquake visited countries, the amount of damage done by it plainly shows that the earthquake was of no ordinary character in our country at least.

We are so much in the habit of regarding earthquakes as exotics, that unnecessary alarm is experienced when one occurs in this country. But every geologist knows that the rocks of the British Isles abound in evidences of earthquake action, although they are seldom to be met with in the latter formed deposits. These evidences of former disturbances are known by the name of 'faults', or dislocations of strata.

Every one of these 'faults' must have occasioned an

earthquake-like shock when it took place. The rocks of the Eastern Counties being formed of clay, chalk, sand and gravel, constitute a very bad medium for earthquake waves to travel along – indeed we may regard them as constituting a capital buffer in this respect.

When the cuttings were taking place in the London Clay at Ray Island, I had occasions to draw attention of geologists to the numerous faults or dislocations exhibited in the sections. The London Clay Cliffs, extending from Felixstowe to Bawdsey are full of evidences of similar earthquake action. Even the more recent strata, soft as they are, afford us illustrations of similar earthquake action.

I repeat that every one of these numberless dislocations, small and great, must have been accompanied by shakings and dislocations of part of the earth's crust where they took place, and it is more than probable that a good many earthquake shocks succeeded each other, possibly after the lapse even of hundreds of years, before some of the largest of these 'faults' could have been formed.

I am of the opinion the earthquake oscillations of Tuesday, which singularly enough seem to have occurred most abundantly over the London Clay area of the Eastern Counties, were really due to one of these 'faults' or 'creeps' to which I have just referred. Consequently, there is not the slightest cause of any alarm that the occurrence of yesterday is a precursor of something worse to follow; it was of altogether a different nature to those dreadful catastrophies of which we heard so much from Ischia and Java last year. Addison used to say that wars were capital things for teaching people geography, and perhaps our East Anglian earthquake may be the means of teaching something about the nature of these natural phenomena.

The pieces still had to be picked up, of course, buildings needed to be repaired, and upset lives returned to their normal tempo. But no one alive on that day would ever forget 'The Great English Earthquake', or question the closing remark of *The Essex Telegraph* on April 26th 1884 that "there is little doubt that if the disturbance had been prolonged for a few brief seconds more the countryside would have been completely destroyed and the loss of life would have been incalculable."

10 A Brief Chronology of British Earthquakes up to the Year 1884

The British Isles, as I have intimated, have been subjected to earthquakes of varying strength and displacement for many centuries. Certain places like Comris in Perthshire, Scotland, have experienced them almost unceasingly, whereas other areas – like Essex, the subject of this book – have only very rarely felt them.

Before closing this book, then, the reader might care to have some details of the more notable of these disturbances. The topic has, in fact, been the subject of several scholarly appraisals, of which Professor Charles Davison's *A History of British Earthquakes* (Cambridge University Press, 1924) is perhaps the most detailed and authoritative. For the reader interested in the full extent and explanation of these phenomena no better work can be recommended. For the benefit of the more casually interested person, though, I have listed below some of the more interesting British earthquakes with relevant details of their impact and effects.

I must stress, however, that this chronology should in no way be taken as exhaustive or complete – a statement which will readily be appreciated when I say that in 1924, when Professor Davison published his book, he was able to list no fewer than 1,190 earthquakes which could be authenticated. To this figure must be added the several hundred which have occurred in the intervening half a century, plus all the much earlier and still unconfirmed reports!

On this subject, *The Times* wrote only this year: "Earthquakes have been known to take place in this country at an average rate of more than 120 a century, although this is certainly a gross underestimate. In the earlier periods a

Some of the major sites where earthquakes have occurred in Britain
– a map prepared by Professor Charles Davison

relatively small and poorly educated population meant that only the larger shocks in the more densely populated areas were observed and reported. The result is that only 98 earthquakes were recorded up to the middle of the eighteenth century, and most of these were described only very briefly by the chroniclers."

103 –

1000. The earthquakes recorded in this 900-year period are all collected in a single rare work comprehensively entitled *A General Chronology Table of Meteors, Weather, Seasons and Diseases* by a Dr Thomas Short, FRS, and published in two volumes in London, 1749. Unfortunately Dr Short does not give the sources on which his reports are based, although he does say that he has spent sixteen years in compiling the list and that "these scraps of history lay scattered in a vast multitude of authors of different designs and professions, as historians, civil, ecclesiastical and political; physicians, divines, naturalists, monks, friars, journalists, travellers, &c." Because of this fact it is impossible to verify the extraordinary details which follow, and most must certainly be questioned:

103. In Somersetshire: "a city was swallowed up, name and all."

132. In the west of Scotland: "men and cattle were swallowed up."

204. "A city in Brecknockshire swallowed up."

261. "A terrible one in Cumberland."

287. "One ruined a great part of Worcester."

394. Wales: "made sad havoc".

424. In Cornwall: "great losses; many killed".

483. At Canterbury: "did great hurt".

534. Somersetshire: "with great damage".

677. At Glasgow: "destroyed many people and houses".

707. Scotland: "did very great mischief".

811. St Andrews: "destroyed most of the town and 1400 people".

844. York: "very hurtful".

974. "A great earthquake took place over all England."

1000. In Cumberland: "swallowed up people, cattle and houses."

From the year AD 1000 earthquakes in Britain can be given with reference sources and these are quoted hereunder.

1060.   On July 4th "there was a great earthquake on the Translation of St Martin" according to the *Anglo-Saxon Chronicle.*

1067.   William of Malmesbury reports in his *Chronicle*: "On the 11th of August, a great earthquake terrified the whole of England by a dreadful marvel, so that all buildings recoiled for some distance and afterwards settled down as before."

1081.   On Christmas Day, in this year, the *Flores Historiarum* says "a great earthquake, accompanied with a terrible subterraneous noise, took place all over England, in a manner contrary to the usual course of nature."

1088.   Henry of Huntingdon and the *Brut Y Tywysogion* both report on "a dreadful earthquake in all the island of Britain" but give no specific date.

1089.   This earthquake on August 11th is noted by no less than eight chroniclers including Symeon of Durham, John de Oxenedes and Roger de Hoveden who writes, "About the third hour of the day, there was a very great earthquake throughout England."

1092.   The *Harlein Miscellany* records that in "the fifteenth year of William Rufus a great earthquake happened in England in the month of April". It is believed that the impact was most strongly felt in London where "strange it was for the doleful and hideous roaring which it yielded forth."

1107.   Coincidentally with a violent earthquake in Italy in the spring, Lincolnshire suffered a shock and the walls of Croyland Church, which was then being built, "gave way, and the south wall was cracked in so many places that the carpenters were obliged to shore it up with timbers till the roof was raised." (Quoted in *The History of the County of Lincoln 1834*.)

1118.   In this year, reports the Irish volume, *Annals of Loch Cé*, there was "a very great earthquake in Sliabh-Elpa, which extinguished many cities, and a multitude of people in them."

1120. On September 28th in the Vale of Trent. "This yeare was a great Earthquake in manie places of England about the thirde houre of the daie," Dr Thomas Short quotes a contemporary chronicler. It overthrew many houses and "buried their inhabitants in the ruins, for it gave daily 10, 17 or 20 shocks."

1129. "On the night of the mass of St Nicholas", records *The Anglo Saxon Chronicle*, "a little before day, there was a great earthquake."

1133. A very violent earthquake was recorded on August 4th by the *Flores Historiarum*: "Earlie in the morning, in manie parts of England, an earthquake was felt, so that it was thought that the earth would have sunke under the feete of men, with such a terrible sound, as was horrible to heare."

1185. Several authorities record a major upheaval in April on either the 15th, 16th or 17th of the month. It was especially felt at Lincoln where many buildings were thrown down including the cathedral. Holinshed says it was "a sore earthquake through all the parts of the land, such a one as the like had not beene heard of in England sithens the beginning of the world."

1186. Matthew of Westminster reports on a disturbance "after the middle of September" which was felt throughout Europe, especially in Calabria, Sicily and England and "in all of which places great structural damage was caused".

1193. Volume I of *The History of Weather* records for this year "a great one [earthquake] that levelled edifices and trees with the ground." No date or locations are given.

1240. The *Annales Monastic* report an undated upheaval felt in many parts of England. "A terrible sound was heard", it says, "as if a huge mountain had been thrown forth with great violence, and fallen in the middle of the sea; and this was heard in a great many places at a distance from each other, to the great terror of the multitudes who heard."

1246. On June 1st "happen'd so great an Earthquake that the like had been seldom seen or heard," says Camden.

Especially felt in Kent where it "overturn'd several churches".

1247.   An earthquake was experienced in several parts of England, "very injurious and terrible in its effects", said Matthew Paris, the chronicler. It was felt especially in London along the banks of the river Thames where buildings were thrown down.

1248.   Matthew Paris also records a disturbance on December 21st in this year, in the west of England. Many churches in Somerset were damaged and the tower of the cathedral at Wells was thrown down. He writes, "This earthquake by which (as was told to the writer of this work by the Bishop of Bath, in whose diocese it occurred) the walls of buildings were burst asunder, the stones were torn from their places, and gaps appeared in the ruined walls, struck great terror into all who heard it ... it was the third which had occurred within three years on this side of the Alps; one in Savoy and two in England; a circumstance unheard of since the beginning of the world, and therefore the more terrible."

1250.   The extraordinary circumstances which accompanied an upheaval at St Albans on December 13th are once more given in some detail by Matthew Paris in the second volume of his works. "On the day of St Lucia, about the third hour of the day, an earthquake occurred at St Albans and the adjacent districts ... where from time immemorial no such event had ever been seen or heard of; for the land there is solid and chalky, not hollow or watery, nor near the sea; wherefore such an occurrence was unusual and unnatural, and more to be wondered at. This earthquake, if it had been as destructive in its effects as it was unusual and wonderful, would have shaken all buildings to pieces; it came on with a trembling motion, and attended by a sound as it were dreadful subterranean thunder. A remarkable circumstance took place during the earthquake, which was this: the pigeons, jackdaws, sparrows and other birds which were perched on the houses and the branches of trees, were seized with fright, as though a hawk was hovering over them, and suddenly expanding their wings, took to flight, as if they were made, and flew backwards and forwards in confusion, but after the trembling motion of the earth and the rumbling noise had ceased, they returned to their usual nests."

1255. September. "In the octave of the feast of St Mary in September, there was an earthquake in Wales, about the hour of the evening tide," says the *Brut y Tywysogion*.

1275. There are varying reports about the actual date of the earthquake in this year which wrecked many churches and destroyed St Michael's at Glastonbury. Matthew of Westminster gives the most likely date as being September 11th, and in William Roper's *Catalogue of British Earthquakes*, the author reports, "A great one felt in Newcastle, dreadful thunder and lightning, a blazing star, and a comet with the appearance of a great dragon, which terrified people."

1319. December 1st. "A general earthquake in England, with great sound and much noise" – *Le Livere de Reis de Engleterre*.

1349. The *Chronica Monasterii de Melsa* says that "during Lent there occurred throughout the whole of England an earthquake so great that the monks at Melsa, while at Vespers, were thrown so violently from their stalls that they all lay prostrate on the ground."

1356. *The History of Weather* reports an upheaval in this year in Ireland with "great loss of people."

1361. The earthquake of 1361 has the distinction of being one of the earliest to be recorded in verse, in *John Hardyng's Chronicle*:

> In the same yere was on sainct Maurys day,
> The great winds and earth quake marvelous,
> That greately gan the people all affraye,
> So dreadful was it then an perelous.

1382. On May 21st occurred one of the strongest of all British earthquakes. Holinshed gives the time as about 1 p.m. "An earthquake in England, that the lyke thereof was never seen in Englande before that daye nor sen" (R. Fabyan). Another report says, "A great earthquake in England ... fearing the hearts of many, but in Kent it was most vehement, where it suncke some Churches, and threw them down to the earth." Holinshed reports that there was a second disturbance on May 24th: "Earlie in the morning, chanced another earthquake, or (as some write) a watershake, being so vehement and violent a motion, that it made the ships in the havens to beat one against the other, by reason whereof they were sore bruised by such knocking together." (On the day of the first shock, John Wycliffe was being tried at Westminster for his opinions on the Bible, and the sudden shock caused the court to break up in alarm: thereafter the assembly was known as the 'Council of the Earthquake'!)

1384.   There appears to have been a severe earthquake in this year, not long after the insurrection of Wat Tyler, although its only record is in a poem contained in a volume called the *Vernon Manuscript* in the Bodleian Library:

And also when this eorthe quok,
  Was non so proud he n' as agast,
And al his jolite forsok
  And though on God whyl that hit last.
And alsone as hit was overpast
  Men wor as wel as thei dude are.
Uche mon in his herte mai cast
  This was a warnying to beware.
Forsoth this was a Lord to drede
  So sudenly mad mon aghast.
Of gold and selver thei tok non hede
  But out of the house ful sone thei past.
Chambres, chimeneys, all to barst,
  Chirches and castels foul gon fare,
Pinacles, steples, to ground hit cast,
  And al was warnyng to beware.

1480.   "A very great earthquake", says Reverend Francis

Blomefield in his *Topographical History of the County of Norfolk* of an upheaval on December 28th which affected most of England and threw down buildings in Norwich and elsewhere.

1508. On September 19th, "A great earthquake in manie places both in England and Scotland" (Holinshed).

1574. At about five o'clock in the evening of February 26th, several counties in the Midlands were affected by a shock which partly destroyed Ruthen Castle, says John Stow's *Anneles of England*.

1580. A boy and girl were killed by falling masonry at Christ Church in London when it was struck by a shock at 6 p.m. on April 6th. St Paul's was also damaged, and the great bell in the Palace of Westminster was set ringing. At Dover the sea was much agitated and a piece of the cliff and the castle wall were thrown down. According to Camden, the earthquake was also felt in France, Belgium and Holland.

1581. On a day at the beginning of April there was "an earthquake not far from York, which in some places strook the very stones out of Buildings, and made the Bells in Churches to jangle", according to Yorkshire historian Sir R. Baker.

1583. A rather bizarre story is recorded in this year from the parish of Hermitage in Dorset. Stow, in his *Anneles of England*, says that "a piece of ground, containing three acres, was torn up by an earthquake, removed from its original station, and thrown over another close to the distance of forty perches." Stow said that the hedges and trees around the field "enclosed it still" but that "it stopped up a highway leading to the market town of Cerne; and that the place from whence this field was torn, resembled a great pit."

1596. According to *The British Chronologist* there was an earthquake this year in Kent "which did great damage to buildings and killed several people."

1608. On the evening of November 8th there took place the shock that "must be reckoned as one of the great Scottish earthquakes", (Professor Charles Davison.)

It affected almost 11,000 square miles and was particularly marked in the county of Fife, and at Dundee, Edinburgh, Glasgow, Aberdeen and Dumbarton. D. Calderwood in his contemporary report notes that at Dumbarton "the people were so affrayed, that they ranne to the kirk ... for they looked presentlie for destruction." At Aberdeen the people were similarly alarmed and the local magistrates and clergymen ordered that the next day should be set aside for fasting and prayer for their deliverance.

1638.   Towards the end of the year there was much damage done by several shocks which were most severely felt in the Chichester district. (Robert Mallet's "Catalogue of Earthquakes" in the *Reports of the British Association.*)

1650.   On an evening in April: "Cumberland and Westmorland were so shaken by an earthquake that people left their houses and fled to the fields", says Dr Thomas Short in his survey.

1678.   People in bed in Staffordshire were awakened by a noise "like flat rumbling" on November 4th, according to Robert Mallet. There were three earth movements in all, each about half an hour apart, which did considerable damage.

1692.   On September 8th between 2 and 3 p.m. there was a violent earthquake, probably focused on Brabant, which was felt throughout much of Europe including Britain. John Evelyn in his *Diary* records that he felt the effects in his house in Surrey and heard that in London "the streets were filled with panic-stricken crowds." (Colchester also apparently felt the impact and the steeple of St Peter's Church in the town was badly cracked.)

1727.   Devon was struck by an upheaval between 4 and 5 a.m. on July 19th as J.C. Cox's *Parish Registers of England* quotes: "All the houses in Exeter did shake with an Earthquake that people was shakt in their beds from one side to the other, and was al over England, and in some places beyond the sea, but doed little damage; tis of a certain truth."

1734.   In August there was an upheaval in Ireland which

destroyed over 100 houses and 5 churches, according to *The British Chronologist*.

1736.   Subterranean noises preceded for several hours a shock at Ochil Hills in Scotland which "rent several houses and put the people to flight". (*The Gentleman's Magazine.*)

1750.   This "year of earthquakes", as Dr W. Stukely called it, was marked by extensive upheavals in February 19th, March 19th and October 11th. The first two were felt particularly in London and the Home Counties; the third affecting the counties of Northampton, Leicester, Rutland, Nottingham, Lincoln and Suffolk. Although some chimneys and walls were thrown down in London and the suburbs on February 19th, there was much heavier damage on March 19th with entire houses being wrecked and "great stones falling from the new spire of Westminster Abbey", according to Robert Mallet. As a result of a ball of fire being seen in the sky immediately after the second occurrence, rumour-mongers began predicting more and still worse earthquakes that year – and one man even managed to convince many Londoners that they would be in dire peril on April 8th. *The Illustrated Police News* reported their reaction: "To avoid the effects of a shock predicted by a madman for April 8th 1750, thousands of persons – particularly those of rank and fortune – passed the night of the 7th in their carriages and in tents in Hyde Park. The poorer classes spent the dreaded night in walking about Lambeth and Lambs' Conduit Fields, on Clapham Common, and Hampstead Heath, and some took up their quarters on the barges and lighters upon the river. Horace Walpole wrote one of his most amusing letters on the eve of this predicted calamity, and in it he mentions the "earthquake gowns" which were especially made to sit up in all night. 'But what will you think' says he, 'of Lady —, Lady —, Lord and Lady —, who go this evening to an inn ten miles out of town, where they are to play brag till five in the morning, and then come back – I suppose to look for the bones of their husbands and families under the rubbish?' " In fact, the only other occurrence that year was in the October in the Midlands when there were four successive shocks, accompanied by a loud noise, but no real damage was done. Nonetheless, all this activity did stir the Royal Society into beginning to take a serious scientific interest in the phenomenon; and the full documentation of earthquakes began.

1757.   The shock in Cornwall on July 15th at 6.30 p.m. is notable in earthquake history as being the first such event to be the subject of a detailed paper. The repott was prepared by the Reverend W. Borlass, a local clergyman, who stated that the epicentre had been near Penzance and the effect had been felt as far away as the Scilly Isles. There had first been a rumbling noise underground, "hoarser and deeper than common thunder", he said, followed by a trembling of the earth "which afterwards waved violently to and fro once or twice." Miners working below ground feared they would be buried alive.

1777.   The earthquake which centred on Rochdale and Manchester at 10.55 a.m. on September 14th was felt over an area of almost 22,000 square miles and was commented on by Dr Johnson, who was staying at Ashbourne in Derbyshire when it happened. " 'Sir,' he said when Boswell told him of the earthquake, 'it will be much exaggerated in public talk; for, in the first place, the common people do not accurately adapt their thoughts to the objects; nor, secondly, do they accurately adapt their words to their thoughts; they do not mean to lie; but, taking no pains to be exact, they give you very false accounts. A great part of their language is proverbial. If anything rocks at all, they say it rocks like a cradle; and in this way they go on.' " (*Boswell's Life of Dr Johnson*, Volume 4).

1790.   Two fissures over 200 feet long and very deep "into which houses and cattle sank" resulted from a disturbance at Ormside, Westmorland at 4 a.m. on February 27th. *The Gentleman's Magazine* reported that there had been a violent shock and a loud explosion.

Later investigators have wondered whether the occurrence might have been a landslip.

1799.   *The Gentleman's Magazine* again reported an earthquake in the last year of the century on the Channel Island of Guernsey. It happened during the night of February 6th and caused "several houses to be rent from top to bottom".

1816.   The blow which struck Scotland at 10.45 p.m. on August 13th is the strongest known in that country. Covering about 38,000 square miles, it did greatest damage in Inverness where chimneys and tiles were flung from roofs, walls were cracked, and the spire on the county jail was broken off. The disturbance was also strongly felt at Perth, Aberdeen, Edinburgh and Glasgow. (See report by T.E. Lauder.)

1839.   Scotland was again affected in this year on October 23rd when two thirds of the country felt the shock. *The Edinburgh Royal Society Transactions* said that the focus was probably Comrie in Perthshire "a place which has suffered more earthquakes than any other in the British Isles." There were still further disturbances in the same locality in 1841 and in July "dykes were thrown down in many places" near Comrie.

1852.   A unique upheaval occurred on November 9th at 4.25 a.m. "In one respect," Professor Davison has written, "this earthquake seems to be unique among British earthquakes, for it was probably felt in all four portions of the United Kingdom. Its disturbed area, so far as can be traced, is 290 miles long from W.N.W. to E.S.E., 245 miles wide, and contains about 56,000 square miles. It includes the whole of Wales, about half of England, the eastern counties of Ireland, and the southern portion of Scotland including Wigtown and Kirkcudbright." In mountainous districts the intensity was "considerable" and damage was caused in a few places in Ireland. Robert Mallet has remarked that there may well have been several slight shocks during both the previous and following nights.

1863.   *The Times* reported that "loud rumbling noises" and some damage was caused by a disturbance on October 6th at about 3.22 a.m. which affected the Midlands, Southern Counties, Wales and Ireland. The tremor was also felt at sea, about twenty miles from Milford Haven. (Hereford was just one of the many towns hit on this occasion – and in the intervening years to 1924 it has felt tremors no less than twenty times, two of which were almost as strong as that at Colchester!)

1869.   During the period from March 15th to 29th, several slight tremors were recorded in East Lancashire and on the border of West Yorkshire. Manchester and Hull were both disturbed more than once, and some damage was done at Newchurch and Haslingden – where the railway station building was put out of operation.

1879.   "A rather strong shock accompanied by a noise like that of a building falling" was the description given by *Nature* magazine of the upheaval in County Donegal on December 6th at about 11.30 p.m. It was also felt in County Tyrone.

1883 –
1884.   A series of minor earthquakes culminating on April 22nd at 9.18 a.m. with – The Great English Earthquake.

POSTSCRIPT

On the day I completed writing this book, Friday January 17th 1975, the following brief item appeared in the columns of *The Daily Telegraph*: "There was an earth tremor on the East Sussex coast yesterday. It was felt along a five mile stretch from Telscombe to Seaford."

I also felt the disturbance very slightly as I sat working in my study at Birch Green, Essex.

Appendix

1 My Escape from the Earthquake

The great majority of letters about the earthquake written at the time to the Essex newspapers – indeed, those to the national papers as well – were not surprisingly from clergymen, professional people and the landed gentry. A considerable number of them have been excerpted in this book, but one which struck me as particularly evocative and well-worth reproducing *in extenso* was that from a well-known Essex dignitary, Sir Charles Du Cane of Braxted Park, Witham. Although some distance from the centre of the disturbance, the reactions in Sir Charles' household must have been typical of millions of others throughout eastern England. The letter was sent to *The Essex Standard*, and I found it, as I mentioned in Chapter 7, in an old family scrapbook ...

Sir – Thinking that an individual experience of yesterday's earthquake may not be uninteresting to your readers, I write to say that yesterday morning at 20 minutes past 9 I was sitting at the writing table in the hall of my house, which is about twelve miles from Colchester on the London side of that town. Suddenly there came a noise which I can only compare to the rumbling of the underground railway combined with the rushing sound of a strong wind, and passing, so far as I could judge, from east to west. At the same moment the whole house was violently shaken, and every bell was set ringing. The strong and compact oak floor of the hall trembled beneath my feet like the deck of a ship in a gale of wind; and some marble columns with busts on the top of them rocked to such an extent that I thought the busts must have fallen. I afterwards found that one of the columns had been displaced nearly an inch from its original position. My coachman, who was washing a brougham in the stable yard close by, states that feeling the ground tremble under his feet, and hearing the glass roof of the conservatory rattle, he looked up at the house which appeared to him to be rocking to and fro. Thinking he was seized with giddiness, he caught hold of the carriage wheel for support, and found that the brougham was also oscillating. Only one clock out of several going in the house, one on the principal staircase, was stopped, at exactly 20 minutes past 9. My impression at the time was that the shock must have lasted about ten seconds, but looking at the very small amount of actual damage done, compared to that of which accounts have been received from Colchester and the immediate neighbourhood, it may possibly have been of less duration. What the consequences would have been had it lasted a few seconds longer I tremble to think. As it was, it was quite sufficient to cause very great alarm to every inmate of the house. The horses, too, in the stables were much frightened, and reared and plunged violently. It is strange, however, to me that with a shock of such apparent strength, so small an amount of damage should have been done. There is a quantity of china on the mantelpiece and against the walls in the different parts of the house, not a piece of which was displaced, nor, with the exception of a crack in a bedroom ceiling and a slight fall of plaster from the drawing-room ceiling and on the staircase, could we find any after sign of what had happened. I may add that almost immediately after the shock, I telegraphed for an architect of great experience, Mr Chancellor, of Chelmsford, who came over in the afternoon, and satisfied himself by careful inspection that the mischief was confined to that of which we had thus seen the outward and visible sign. I have had no previous experience of earthquakes, and most sincerely trust I may never be destined to renew that of yesterday. Meanwhile I cannot feel too thankful that my house and all belonging to it have escaped so easily.

I remain, Sir, yours faithfully,
        CHARLES DU CANE
                Braxted Park, Witham, Essex, April 23rd, 1884.

2   The Mystery of the Stinking Black Sea

Among the many items of correspondence and documentary evidence which I received from people all over eastern England while researching this book, there was perhaps none more intriguing than that from Mrs A.M. Osborne of Colchester. She sent me details of the story her late father had told her of the earthquake – and pointed out that "although I have read many accounts of the event, in none of them can I recall any mention of the stinking black sea which occurred at the time." Nor, indeed, could I or any of my other informants. Nonetheless, the statement is a fascinating record by an eyewitness and I reproduce it exactly as it was given. If any reader can throw some more light on to the mystery of the strange sea and the dead fish I would be very pleased to hear from them.

Mrs Osborne writes:

My father's name was Walter Page. He was born on the 17th of February, 1870 and baptised at the little church at Layer Breton – one of the many churches hit by the earthquake. Later his family moved to Virley, but I do not know how old he was then.

His father died in April 1884, at the early age of 41, leaving a wife with several small children to support. My father, who was then fourteen, had to work on the land, and his only brother John was at sea. The family was not desperately poor while my grandfather was alive, for all the children were sent to school with their penny or twopence per week. But all this stopped when their father died.

On the morning of the earthquake, my father was walking with an older man back to work after breakfast, along the headland of a field at the bottom of Middleford Hill, Wigborough. Suddenly the earth shook underfoot and the high hedge laid down on the ground and then stood up again. The older man fell over and he said the earth moved up between his fingers as he lay on the ground.

The field was quite near a small farmhouse and some cottages, and at once there was a fearful noise – as the tiles and chimney pots came hurling down. Women rushed screaming out of their houses clutching small children who were also crying, fearing the end of the world had come.

Inside the houses pictures fell from the walls, plates and dishes fell from the shelves and smashed on the floor. And to make it seem worse, all the church bells began to ring.

No more work was done in the fields as the men ran to their homes to see to the damage and help their wives. The young men also went around to see the damage and to help if they could.

At the time of the shock, my grandmother was breaking a large lump of coal outside the back door and when the window fell out she thought a lump of coal had broken it. Great was her amazement to see the coal unbroken and no window!

The garden of my grandparent's cottage ended at the bank of Salcott Creek and when the tide came in the water was black, thick and foul smelling and everywhere it left dead fish. The water remained black for several days.

Fourteen cottages stood between the bottom of Middleford Hill and The Kings Head at Wigborough and only six were safe for people to live in. Today I think there are only three. The people who had to leave their homes (some were relatives of my father) moved away – several of them going across the River to the Southminster area.

A person can usually tell where one of these cottages stood, for often there is an old plum or apple tree as part of the hedge – or the hedge does not seem quite the same as the usual hedgerow.

My father was eighty-two-years-old when he died, but he always remembered the day 'the hedge laid down and got up again', and the sea that was 'black and stinking'.

3 Verses on the Late Earthquake in the Eastern Counties

Apart from the official report of the Essex Field Club, the only other volumes published on the earthquake were two small booklets produced by the Colchester printer, Frederic Wright. The first of these, *A Full Account of the Calamitous Earthquake in East Essex*, was an unembellished reprint of the news stories which had appeared in *The Essex Telegraph* on Saturday, April 26th and the subsequent two weekends. The second was a collection of poems by a local writer, Caroline Mary Prior of Colchester. The little work was entitled *Verses on the late Earthquake in the Eastern Counties and Other Subjects* and apart from the title piece, consisted mainly of 'poems of sentiment' with titles like "Examination of Deaf and Dumb Children" and "Friendship with Jesus". The collection seems to have been popular with local readers and ran to at least two editions. Here is the title work:

Preface.
What I have said of the Earthquake,
   I trust may comfort some:
Our God does not His own forsake,
   Though fears may sometimes come.

If words of mine should any bless,
   The Praise to God belongs:
He can make glad the wilderness
   And deserts echo songs.

THE EARTHQUAKE

Eighteen-hundred and Eight-four!
   Oh most eventful year!
We never felt so weak before,
   And never knew such fear.

Lo, on one Tuesday morning, bright,
   A visitation came,
Our hearts were seized with sudden fright,
   For "Earthquake" was its name.

The April sun gave kindly light
   This twenty-second day;
Thank God that we had passed the night,
   And that He was our stay.

At twenty minutes, 'twas, past nine,
   The wondrous trembling came;
We never shall forget the time –
   Bells rang, clocks dumb became.

Great noises overhead were heard,
   Loud rumblings underground;
Our houses rocked, the earth was stirr'd,
   We felt awe most profound.

And from the church at Lion Walk
   The spire fell to the ground;
And in its fall of love did talk
   That none was hurt around.

Before it pointed to the sky,
   Then preached humility.
It used to say, "Let aims be high",
   Then said, "From pride be free".

It helpless was to raise itself;
    And so, dear friends, are we –
From falling could not keep itself,
    Nor, without help, can we.

Fond mothers of their children thought
    (Before themselves) about;
Their infants in their arms they caught,
    And then with them rushed out.

Meanwhile, the chimneys and the slates
    Were falling ev'ry way;
Though people were outside their gates,
    No one was hurt that day.

Much of man's work it did undo
    In a short space of time;
The voice of God proclaimed through
    It all, "The earth is Mine".

So when we would salvation win,
    Good works are shatter'd down;
At "Jesus only" for our sin,
    Justice will cease to frown.

It took its solemn journey forth
    In mercy God looked down,
Protected us, deferr'd His wrath,
    And spar'd our ancient town.

Not only dear old Colchester,
    But we found Wivenhoe
Was more than we a sufferer,
    And Church at Langenhoe.

Peldon and Mersea felt its power;
    Abberton, Fingringhoe;
Of bricks and tiles had quite a shower –
    They of the earthquake know.

A cup and saucer were knocked out
    Of a poor woman's hand*
Bricks from a chimney fell about
    The spot where she did stand.

* Mrs Dyer, a charwoman, was at Mr Cater's butcher, of Magdalen Street, Colchester, when a chimny fell into the room and knocked a cup and saucer out of her hand without injuring her.

A man fetched water from a well*
A brick fell in his pail;
The man escaped God's care to tell
Of His poor creature frail.

Dear Friends, my time would fail to tell
All the hair-breadth escapes.
Our God's love is, we know full well,
Better than wine from grapes.

London and Ipswich felt the shock,
And many towns we know:
It truly was a solemn knock
At our heart's door, I trow.

At Wigborough, the Vicar good,
For explanation wrote;
But soon the Voice he understood
God's warning did denote.

Oh! may the solemn warning be
Salvation's chariot,
But sinners from dread worth may flee,
Whose deaths God willeth not.

"Awake to righteousness," awake!
Slumber in sin no more;
Forgiveness ask for Jesus sake;
Repent, believe, adore!

A woman asked a Minister†
"What is it?" and he said,
"It is an earthquake," unto her,
Whose thoughts to Jesus fled.

"I think it will bring me to Christ" –
She spoke as from her heart –
I trust she's found him and rejoic'd
For Christ does joy impart.

---

* A labourer of Peldon was fetching water when a brick fell in his pail. He was uninjured.

† The Reverend E. Miller, Pastor of Headgate Chapel, Colchester, was asked by a woman who had left her house and gone into the street, "What is it?" Mr Miller replied, "So far as I can judge, it is an earthquake." She then made the remark, "I think it will bring me to Christ."

Though earthly buildings were thrown down
   And temples made with hands,
May God fix in new hearts His throne
   And draw us by love's bands.

We thank Thee, God, for love display'd
   By man to fellow man;
For kindness shown to hearts dismay'd
   When low their comforts ran.

May God bless those who helped to raise
   Again the poor man's house,
And sacred Temples for His praise,
   To bid the wand'rers come.

Oh, may our still spared lives, dear Lord,
   Be more than ever thine;
In all our weakness strength offord
   And "cause Thy face to shine".

Accept our thanks for mercy shown
   When danger came so near;
Our humble homage at Thy throne
   We pay in reverent fear.

Yet while we fear Thee, we would love,
   And our poor love would tell;
May we sing in Thy home alone,
   Thou hast "done all things well."

Acknowledgements

During the research and writing of this book I was helped by a great many people, and while all have earned my thanks I should particularly like to mention the following: Mr Alfred Mason, Mrs J. Stubbings, Mr T.B. Millatt, Mr F.B. Raymond, Mr S.W. Goff, Mrs N.G. Chapman, Reverend Paul Faunch, Mr James Maxwell, Mrs J.G. Eve, Mrs Muriel Privett, Dr N.V. Baker, Mrs Marjorie C. Taylor, Mrs A.M. Osborne, Mr Sidney Barron, Mrs Winifred Sach, Miss Vera Day, Miss D.M. Simmons, Miss H.E. Haward, Marjorie Bucke, Mr C.E. Martin, Mrs M.J. Clarke, Mrs K.E. Smith, Miss Margaret Appleton, Miss Eileen Grubb, Miss Beatrice Simons, Mrs Bertha Smith, Mrs M.A. Roberts, Mr Peter Sherry, Miss M. Ellis, Mrs E. Bell, Colonel R.R. Leaning, Mrs S.A. Mills, Mr Charles Crisp, Mr J.J. Maling, Mr Varley Gunn, Miss N.K. Smith, Mr John B. Gordon and Mrs M.S. Carter. Also Mr P.R. Gifford, Colchester Borough Librarian, Mr David Clarke, Curator of the Colchester & Essex Museum and Mr K.C. Newton, the Essex County Archivist, and his staff at the Essex Records Office, Chelmsford, the editors of *The East Anglian Magazine, The Essex Countryside, East Anglian Daily Times, Evening Gazette*, Colchester, *Colchester Express* and *Essex County Standard*. Material was also contributed by the Essex Naturalists Society, and the various newspapers and journals which I referred to are all mentioned in the text. Finally, I must thank Chris Scott who supervised the copying of the illustrations which appear in the book, and my wife, Philippa, who typed the manuscript and was both my keenest critic and encourager. As for all my friends at the Hare & Hounds public house at Birch where the idea was first raised — here at last is the reason that kept me away from the bar for so many weeks!

Peter Haining

Index